C000271709

for Anth

morphogenesis /mor·pho·gen·e·sis/ (mor″fo-jen′ĕ-sis) the evolution and development of form, as the development of the shape of a particular organ or part of the body, or the development undergone by individuals who attain the type to which the majority of the individuals of the species approximate.

http://medical-dictionary.thefreedictionary.com/morphogenesis

———

http://www.wisegeek.com/what-is-morphogenesis.htm

Table of Contents

There are further resources as well as information relating to the next in this series of books and they can be found at www.TreeMorphogenesis.com

Tree Morphogenesis

Introduction

Whatever you think that you know about trees, hard learned facts or assumptions, please put them aside and look forward to getting a new perspective on them including some new insights that I hope will both surprise as well as profoundly influence and guide you in your dealings with trees in future.

I have what I consider to be a wonderful job. In fact I believe it to be the best job in the world bar none. Every day is a different challenge, a new location and a new set of logistical problems. The physical challenges keep me fit, the mental challenges test me in many ways and the ever attendant risks keep me aware of just how precious life is.

I remember a conversation from just after I had established my tree contracting company (in early 1985). A friend asked me "You play rugby, fly hang gliders, ride a motorcycle like a maniac and you climb trees for a living. Have you got a death wish?". Well, I thought about this for a moment then told him this in response "No. But I never feel so alive as when I can feel my heart beating like its trying to get out of my chest".

I suppose that makes me an adrenaline junkie and therefore particularly suitable for a career in tree care. To balance that however I have a very real and healthy fear of heights. So I'm definitely not risk averse but I am acutely risk aware and I derive great personal and professional satisfaction from effectively managing those risks and conquering my own entirely rational fear.

More than that though, I have dedicated my professional life to studying trees and they never fail to intrigue and inspire me as I learn ever more about them. So I started in high tree work because I'm a showoff (who liked to challenge himself in oh so many ways) but I stayed with trees because they led me on a journey of discovery that this book is part of. A journey which is still ongoing.

The establishment, maintenance and care of trees, "Arboriculture", is in the middle of what will become seen as its renaissance period right now. That is due to the growth of tree research which in turn is the result of massive interest in green issues and consequent investment in the science of tree understanding.

Think of the emerging science of tree care it this way. When I started in the mid 1980's I estimate that Arboriculture was at about the same stage of evolution that medical science was at, in the Napoleonic wars. In other words, we knew how to recognise diseases and disorders and we knew where to amputate but with very basic standards of hygiene.

Then came Alex Shigo with his groundbreaking books starting with "A New Tree Biology" and his mantra "Touch Trees". That book started the process by which the science of Arboriculture dramatically increased the speed of its evolution.

Arboriculture is now growing at a rapid rate but even so, it is still in its infancy. That means that Arboriculture is one of the most exciting areas of science because it is still possible to make major discoveries and breakthroughs that significantly influence tree care and help people to understand trees a bit better.

I say "a bit better" but in reality there seems to me to be a gulf of misunderstanding between people and trees. Recognising that, the Tree Morphogenesis Project is my final and greatest challenge as an Arboriculturist. For the first time I am working on trees in the broadest sense, by working remotely on the understanding and the minds of the tree owner through this book. That means in this instance, I'm working on You.

So open your mind and prepare to be entertained and hopefully convinced by new and novel ideas and discoveries that I hope will make natural sense to you as I describe them in a sequence that will build your insights into your own trees towards a specific practically applicable conclusion.

The ideas that I present here have never been released before and as far as I am aware, are not available anywhere else.

Some of my theories are not "scientifically" tested, or at least, not rigorously and independently tested. They are just my own beliefs and are based almost entirely on my own seat of the pants observations which fuelled my further research and testing in the field. They may be new ways of looking at old things but sometimes a review is the best way to move forward.

I hope that by coming to understand them better as I explain, you will also come to a more informed understanding and trust your trees so that you will be more comfortable with them in your garden with minimal maintenance if any at all.

You should also be aware that I am a conscientious objector to tree surgery. That is because as presently practiced, it is at best a compromise. So in spite of the fact that you can reclaim the cost of this book against any Cheshire Tree Surgeons quote, this book is not designed to get people placing work with my company. Quite the opposite in fact, because by stripping away the misunderstandings that exist relating to trees, I hope that most current tree surgery practices will become somewhat obsolete. That will only be the result if well informed clients (engaging with contractors to obtain tree surgery services), simply stop asking for them.

Some arcane practices will persist but they will be recognised for the severe compromises that they represent for the tree. By understanding how they fail the tree (by failing to consider how evolution has designed the tree), you instantly move to a more sympathetic conceptual model and method of managing your trees.

Personally, I feel that if I have taken the time to explain what I believe is in the best interests of the tree to the client and they choose to do something else, at least I have passed off my duty of care to describe the most sympathetic and effective tree management to them. Most contractors will not take the time to explain why a particular pruning regime will damage a tree because ultimately that will cost them money, so you have to work that out for yourself, then you can ask for management that is more sympathetic to your trees and more cost effective to you. Like good lawyers, tree owners need to know the right answer to the questions that they might put to contractors.

I believe that the ideas presented here will sound and feel entirely credible and logical to you because they pass the "common sense" test. I am also committed to giving you the strong impression that you have come to an informed and detailed understanding of how trees grow. You will also be able to visualise how they adapt through their lives and "read" their life story, in the structures that they create.

That is the outcome that I am trying to achieve here, to develop your informed understanding of how your own trees grow and change through the phases of their lives and show you just how evolution has shaped them.

The insights do not end with the trees because one of the things that I have also discovered concerns one way that the human brain works in relation to trees. That discovery convinced me that we all instinctively know far more about trees than you would ever believe was possible.

The message that I hope every reader realises is that we should trust and actually use our instincts far more than we do.

In this book I would like to start the process of unveiling just how much you know already and I will reveal to you just how valuable and profound your own pre-existing knowledge is. So if as you progress, the things I relate sound somehow familiar to you that might be the process of re-awakening what you already know, in action. In fact, I am trying to give you confidence in your pre-existing understanding, of trees and to do that I will have to trick you in order to get you to use the senses that I want you to realise in yourself. More on that later because I will be saving the best for last.

The broad principle that I am following here is, to give you some practical and technical insights into trees that will "feel" credible and understandable to you, then when I have delivered some ways for you to see trees differently than you do now, I will reveal to you how you can realise what you already know, by looking at them differently.

I do expect you to be no less than surprised and delighted by the result because I will demonstrate in a very practical way that will show you just how closely we have evolved in association with trees and how that evolution left its psychological mark on us. That's at the end of this book and I urge you to not flip to the last chapters prematurely.

The new ideas about tree form and structure that I present here are required reading before the last chapter so for now just look forward to it, expect it and feel cheated if I should fail to deliver fully on this particular commitment.

I want to start this journey by showing you some morphological traits that I have discovered which are the foundation of this concept and then build on those foundations, in the process gradually building your knowledge, insights and familiarity with trees.

I want you to get more comfy with your trees in every sense and that comfort will only come when you better understand them. So I will show you how 500 Million years of evolution have led to the tree structures that we see today because by understanding that and the benefits that trees derive from the growth strategy that I have unravelled and described for you, you will have made the first and greatest leap in your technical understanding of trees as dynamic structures.

After the second chapter, you will literally see trees subtly but profoundly differently than you do now. In fact, you will begin to be able to "read" a tree and its natural history.

Then in Chapter 3, I will explain another concept that is important foundation knowledge and that is hidden in a question that has never before been asked as far as I am aware. The answer reveals the depth of misunderstanding that exists in modern Arboriculture.

In Chapter 4, I will explain another phenomenon that I consider to be profoundly important to tree care and absolutely essential to a holistic approach to considering trees as structures and in the conception of truly sympathetic tree care.

If you are a layperson, this is written for you. If you are an Arborist, this contains information that you have never seen anywhere before, information that you will find essential to do your job because this is most definitely "applied adaptive research" of a kind that you do every day whether you realise it or not. In fact, if you are an Arborist this information is designed to do nothing less than revolutionise what you do for a living.

Then in the 9th chapter, once you can see how trees grow, I will reintroduce you to yourself, through your own perception of trees.

This work follows a simple business ethic that I follow as closely as I can. Quite simply, I always try to give my clients enough information for them to come to an informed decision.

These new insights into trees are specifically for tree owners first and foremost because it is those informed tree owners who can transform tree care most easily. Those informed tree owners can change Arboriculture overnight (at least, for themselves they can) by simply commissioning the kind of tree care that they, their heirs and their trees need and deserve but to do that you need the "informed decisions" that this book can give you.

It is funny to me all this had a simple revelation in origin which was, I saw a shape preserved in a mature tree. Then I looked around and I saw exactly the same thing in different trees, of many different species and even many different families of trees.

In all I saw the shape of the young tree, preserved and frozen in time and space, within the shape of the mature tree. That was the first step in my journey.

That seems so long ago that I had actually forgotten the first glimpse until now but that and then a whole series of little intuitive leaps, testing and measuring over decades led to this book. I really hope that this book has meaning for you and of course, I hope that you like it. In fact, at the end I will ask you to review the book so that I can make the next one even better.

David Lloyd-Jones

Chapter 1

28 years ago when I set out to become a tree surgeon, I knew nothing about trees.

I was actually on Maggie Thatcher's Enterprise Allowance Scheme which proved to be just the leg up that I needed in very practical ways, so I was very pleased to hear that a similar scheme is being tested again.

Enterprise Allowance gave me funds to allow me to do a basic course in Arboriculture and I was very lucky to have been taught by two truly memorable lecturers at Reeseheath College of Agriculture, namely Geoff Scaife and Rhod Taylor. They sparked an interest and then fed that interest, being both natural and highly effective teachers.

In my ignorance, (when enrolling for my first City & Guilds course), I distinctly remember thinking "Yes, trees. Give it 6 months to get my head around the subject, learn everything there is to learn about trees and this can be my job for the next five years". How naïve those initial expectations sound to me now because I was of course, profoundly ignorant.

After the first 6 months of that block release college course all I was painfully aware of was just how little I knew about trees. The full scope of my ignorance was previously unrealised but by the end of that course I knew enough to daunt me. So it was fortunate that when I started, I didn't know what I didn't know because if I had appreciated that, I might have been deterred from taking those early steps.

It seemed that the more I learned, the more I became aware of all the things that I didn't know and that, I am very pleased to say, is still the case today. However, at that time, far from being overwhelmed, I was challenged by the scope of the learning task because fortunately, by that point, I had also found myself to be absolutely fascinated by trees. Climbing them daily, my life actually depended on understanding them and there is no more visceral connection than one based on survival. I needed to understand them.

My earlier education, wherein I showed interest and aptitude in physical sciences, maths and art, all combined to prove useful all of a sudden. That, and a strong innovative streak that came from working on and rebuilding motorcycles in my generally misspent youth also proved valuable. My life and the various skills that I had accumulated suddenly made sense in tree surgery and my independent (some would say "bloody minded") attitude enabled me to find my own solutions to problems.

Another thing that initially slowed my progress was that I came into Arboriculture without working for anybody else. I had no practical experience whatsoever.

If I had worked as an employee for another tree surgeon I would have been shown the ropes and taught so many tips and tricks covering many day to day things that have to be done correctly in order to safely and efficiently remove or prune a tree. In the end those simple things took me many months to work out for myself.

And I should also say that I went in at the deep end. The image below shows me up a 120' Beech tree, late in the process of sectionally dismantling it and roping it down into a small garden. This technically challenging takedown was just my sixth contract and looking at the image I am still amazed to this day that I was able to complete it at all.

I look for all the world like a "Nit" and I should explain that because the camera angle is looking up, there is another 30' of trunk obscured behind the hedge. It was a big, broad spreading tree that was mostly gone by the time somebody snapped this and if ever there was a true test of my courage and determination, this was it.

In reality, I didn't have the experience to tackle such a job but the "B" side of my general lack of experience was that I had to get very used to creating my own solution. Those solutions were sometimes quite good, even innovative and some of the concepts that this book delivers have their origins in the problem solving mindset that I had to adopt.

That turned something I did wrong (my lack of practical experience) into many things that I did right by creating my own, sometimes unique new solutions to old problems.

The other real strength that I have is my laziness. Yes, it may surprise you but I admit it, I am as lazy as the day is long.

Fortunately for my business however, I also firmly believe in the old saying.......
"If you want to find the easiest way to do a given task, ... give it to your laziest man"!

Below is a poor quality image showing a five tonne tree stump being lifted off our wagon. In 1987 we were working on the great storm damage at the City of London Cemetary and Crematorium in Forest Gate, East London. While that project, (clearing the hundreds of storm damaged trees, felling trees that were too damaged to retain and then pruning many hundreds of other trees that were damaged in that storm) gave me many insights into how wind affects trees and how trees are designed to be affected by wind, it also included some elements that tested our dogged determination.

In this one image the evidence of my team's collective ability to graft is clearly shown. Why? Well this is the largest tree stump that we ever dug out, by hand!

It was another test and it was a test that I did not enjoy. It's all well and good being the contractor who is prepared to work harder, work longer and cheaper, but those sort of operational edges ultimately test ones motivation. Creative laziness however engages innovation in such a way that it can multiply the effectiveness of dogged determination and hard work making them more effective and more joyful.

Creative laziness in action.

"Give it to your laziest man" Never a truer word was spoken in jest for I am that man and I will innovate like crazy to make a job more effective for my clients, hopefully easier, quicker and therefore more cost effective.

That ethic can dramatically help any entrepreneur so I still follow it whenever I can. It's also fun and has produced numerous competitive edges that I have marketed over the years. So I advocate "Creative Laziness" as an effective business strategy.

Laziness expressed as innovation and enterprise is surely a profound contradiction but also an effective one because as a direct result, it leads to refinements and breakthroughs that are in themselves the reward for innovation, which in my case are ultimately, rewards for laziness. This is a bit tongue in cheek but I'm sure you get that.

I have always invested time and energy working "on" my various businesses rather than just dedicating my time to working "in" them. I regularly get lost working in my businesses but the perspective and clarity that come from standing back and working on them, develops the concepts and principles on which the business is based so that the business moves forward, evolves and hopefully, improves the services it delivers.

Fact. If you don't occasionally work "ON" your business, you will for ever work "IN" your business.

Creative laziness continued…

So what started as my attempt to get a "trade" with some hands on skills that I could sell to people and earn money, ended up becoming my vocation and my all consuming passion. Most importantly for my life long career, trees would become a way that I would express myself both technically and professionally.

Without trees, I do not have any idea where else I would have found such an outlet for my ambitions, my physical skills as well as my mindset and interests. The result is that I am left feeling profoundly lucky to have found my true vocation and to have been able to pursue it and continue my own research (thereby continually feeding my curiosity which maintained my interest in trees) throughout my career.

So you see, I know just how overwhelming it can be to even begin to study trees in the detail that you need to in order to understand them because I have done the traditional route. It was long and hard. However now, with the experiences that I have gained teaching Arborists my techniques, I also know how to overcome that steep learning curve very quickly and very easily with some wonderfully simple new insights into trees and specifically, how they grow. That is because this book started out as a training manual that I gave new climbers to read before I would take them up into a tree to show them.

One of the things I was always looking out for were the simple rules that trees grow by, specifically so that I could reveal them to the guys working for me in order to give them insights that would make them better, more effective and more sensitive Arborists.

Teaching the information that an Arboriculturist needs in order for them to be an effective sympathetic tree pruner, presented a problem to me. It typically took a year to complete even a basic Arboriculture study course. I had to train up the people working with me, regardless of their pre-disposition to traditional learning so that they would all be able to understand and follow the specifications that I put together for clients and I had to deliver that understanding to them as fast as I could.

That problem is compounded because there is a process of informed decisions that are implicit in the tree management process that I describe here. So this has to be understandable to the layperson and relatively inexperienced Arborist. It has to be technically accurate in the background science but deliver understanding that would lead to client and arborist understanding explicitly what sympathetic tree pruning, "Reduction Via Thinning" (RVT) is all about.

I realised that to a degree, what I had been taught at college had actually got in the way of my experiencing a tree and had obscured some simple profound truths by burying me in endless technical detail. That revelation convinced me that the information in this book is in reality the most important first building block of tree knowledge and therefore is the very first thing that an Arborist needs to learn. I believe that because I think I have described some fundamental organising principles of almost all woody plants and they are so fundamental that they have been missed even though they form a solid foundation of insights into trees on which all other knowledge and tree services can be built.

Further to that, as these insights are so readily attainable, they have the capacity to ignite the interests of a budding Arborist and the interested tree owner or naturalist.

The implications of those organising principles are huge because by describing those very simple and almost universal rules by which trees grow, I dramatically improved understanding in my Arborists and thereby improved the quality and reliability of service that the people working with me provided for my clients. Many of them had little or no Arboricultural training whatsoever, but they quickly became sensitive and effective at managing trees.

Those fundamental principles are the bones of this book along with the implications that they have for tree care and truly sympathetic tree management. The strength of this work is in the practical application of these principles because this is about both understanding trees and working on them and with their owners, in the real world.

I hope that another strength of this work is that I have taken the tree's point of view so to speak. As such I have tried to understand and describe facets of the tree and its life that would have meaning for the tree. Right now you have no idea why I believe that that is a paradigm shift but by the end of this short book, I hope you will.

You will understand and be able to read a tree's life in it's morphology and by doing that you will be able to see just how the tree and it's evolution, has designed the gradual and progressive failure that the tree will go through as it ages.

You will see the broad truths about trees and how they mould their shape and their lives and those broad universal truths will be a good foundation of simple understanding on which your specific and technical tree knowledge and any management that you specify for your tree, will quite naturally build.

Let me put it to you this way, by the end of this, you will either be informed and intrigued to learn more about trees or you will just be informed, but your trees and you will benefit from the information in this book.

Look at trees differently. See trees differently, understand and therefore trust trees more. These are all bold claims that I hope you will revisit at the end to see if I have nailed them all. They are in fact my commitment to the purpose of this book and my test as a committed Arboriculturist.

Oh yes, the shape in the mature tree that I mentioned…. Well, when I first saw things clearly what I saw was the shape of a young tree perfectly preserved in the structure of the older tree. I spent years trying to understand why and how that might happen.

Unlike me, you get to find out all of the answers in just a few short hours.

Creative laziness got this tree safely down and on the back of our wagon in under 2 hours and the whole job, 4 hours. Without the crane, at least 2 days work for the same team.

In fact, if memory serves we did another 3 jobs that day.

Chapter 2

A study of one tree and its life stages.

In this chapter I want to try to deliver a skill that you can develop and enjoy. Specifically a skill that has the potential to literally change the way that you "see" trees.

In various ways I like to think of it as "seeing the tree in time". That sounds simplistic so let me elaborate slightly because there are different ways in which that phrase can be interpreted.

By "seeing the tree in time", I mean, seeing the tree as the culmination of millions of generations of that tree's species, evolving through "time". That can be a useful perspective when considering what aspects of a tree species growth, might represent an evolutionary advantage by understanding the aspects of growth that characterise that particular species. Understanding those underlying evolved advantages helps guide how that particular species might be managed.

I also mean seeing the tree, in its time. That is, one snap shot of a series, all forming its life. That can be a useful perspective when considering the individual tree and the point to which it has arrived in its life when determining what could be done to manage it.

As individual organisms we live and change through time but as a species we evolve through time. Therefore understanding how a tree species has evolved is different to understanding how the individual has grown as an expression of the broad characteristics of its species in the location that it occupies.

Trees have evolved for 500 million years (give or take a hundred million years or so) and for 99% of that time they have not had to contend with humans because we didn't exist.

Until the last 30,000 years when we humans proliferated and developed stone then metal axes, the land would have developed and changed from treescapes to grasslands and then back again, for the most part very slowly save for periodic natural fluctuations in the climate.

As a general rule, trees would have had to compete and survive within a woodland so it helps to understand what the tests and opportunities of that environment were for a young tree in their original natural habitat.

Trees growing in the primeval woodland would have first had to establish in the shade of the forest floor, waiting as they do for a large tree to fall and create a clearing and a gap in the high canopy into which the young tree can establish itself.

Then, to achieve the high canopy the opportunistic young tree has to make sure that everything that it does helps it to grow upwards at the maximum rate of growth which that example of that species can achieve in that location with the resources available.

It is classical survival of the fittest race to the upper canopy because the first to achieve the high canopy wins and grows on to full maturity, great age and reproduction. Such trees are consequentially well represented by their offspring and therefore their contribution to the gene pool is also significant. They are the winners of that generation that directly influence the subsequent generations.

So once the gap in the canopy is created, every resource that the young tree can obtain is used to grow into the light and the young tree does that with absolute focus and it grows to a height that will be limited by the height of the mature trees around the clearing but that's the sprint race that evolution designed and honed "young" trees form.

However, in maturity, the winners of that race (the trees that get their canopies in the direct sunlight), no longer need to grow so strongly upward. At that point in fact strong upward growth it is no longer such an advantage at all.

From that point on, the advantages that come from spreading rather than growing ever upward takes over and by changing its growth patterns, the primeval tree species adapted themselves to the different adversities and the opportunities that come from achieving the high canopy.

Well that adaptive process leaves its shadow on the structure of mature trees and that is what I saw in lots of trees and eventually, that is what I came to understand. Seeing it, I gradually realised why it was so and as I researched further I saw the many evolutionary and strategic benefits that trees get from it.

I am going to explain to you exactly how I believe that process occurs and how it profoundly affects the shape and form of the trees in your garden. I will also show why it should influence the way that you manage those trees in the interests of both tree health, efficiency and (most importantly) the best, the most effective as well as the least detrimental ways that you can use your tree care budget.

I think that it is important that I tell this story without resorting to the use of unnecessary jargon or technicalities unless such jargon or a technical concept is important and absolutely necessary to deliver the insights that I am presenting here their importance to the tree.

The technicalities are certainly there because trees are endlessly complex organisms when you start looking at them in ever more close detail, but the things that I have discovered and the benefits that the trees get from them are not hard to understand.

Anyway, let me start by telling the illustrated story of just one tree.

It is one entirely unremarkable tree and its life story will be told, with emphasis on the things that influenced it over its life and literally helped create the subtle variations in this tree's unique morphology.

First, a bit of essential technical jargon "morphology".

Let me just explain the word "morphology" for a moment and only because it is important that you come to understand what it really means. As I said, I will keep jargon to the minimum, but this is important jargon that will come up again and again so it's necessary otherwise I wouldn't bother you with it.

Wikipedia.com – Morphology.
In biology, morphology is a branch of bioscience dealing with the study of the form and structure of organisms and their specific structural features.
This includes aspects of the outward appearance (shape, structure, colour, pattern)[8] as well as the form and structure of the internal parts like bones and organs. This is in contrast to physiology, which deals primarily with function. Morphology is a branch of life science dealing with the study of gross structure of an organism and its component parts.

I know that some people don't like Wikipedia so here is a link to another academically acceptable resource *[http://www.britannica.com/EBchecked/topic/392797/morphology]* see below.
morphology, in biology, the study of the size, shape, and structure of animals, plants, and microorganisms and of the relationships of the parts comprising them. The term refers to the general aspects of biological form and arrangement of the parts of a plant or an animal. The term anatomy also refers to the study of biological structure but usually suggests study of the details of either gross or microscopic structure. In practice, however, the two terms are used almost synonymously.
Typically, morphology is contrasted with physiology, which deals with studies of the functions of organisms and their parts; function and ... (100 of 6,319 words)

So morphology is about the structure of the organism in total including its structural features. It covers how those mechanical parts of a tree grow, develop and work in the broadest sense. It is therefore an holistic concept because it is concerned with the whole organism and how it is arranged structurally.

At the point at which we pick up its life story, the tree that I want to illustrate for you has not been established long. It is a "young tree" in the first image and at approx 18 feet tall I suppose that in human terms, it is the tree equivalent of a gangly teenager.

In the environment in which its genetic line has evolved the young tree would typically have sat in the relative dark of the woodland floor, waiting and clinging on to life in the shade until an opportunity changed its potential as a large tree failed and created the clearing in which it would have the chance to grow up and into a tall mature form.

The tree in this study however is in an open space within our modern world but that context means nothing to the tree, it will grow exactly in the ways that its evolutionary path has moulded it to grow in response to the opportunities and limitations presented by the site as its genetic line has for hundreds of millions of years.

The first drawing in this sequence shows the tree as a young tree and the key part of any such tree is their Apical bud. You see, the Apical bud (the top bud usually on a central shoot in a young tree) controls the tree in subtle but profound ways.

The process by which the Apical bud controls a tree in a process is called Apical Dominance and yes, Apical Dominance is the next bit of essential jargon.

Wikipedia says about Apical Dominance - In <u>plant physiology</u>, **apical dominance** *is the phenomenon whereby the main central* <u>stem</u> *of the* <u>plant</u> *is dominant over (i.e., grows more strongly than) other side stems; on a branch the main stem of the branch is further dominant over its own side branchlets.*

The apical bud subjugates all other side branches by producing growth hormones that reach and affect all parts of the tree. In fact, in this instance I think those growth hormones should be more accurately described as growth *"regulators"* because the Apical bud forces the lateral branches to support the apical bud by NOT competing with it for upward growth. It hormonally subjugates and controls the lateral branches.

In this way the single Apical bud controls and influences all growth of the young tree.

So "growth" hormones are just that, but primarily for the Apical bud itself because they promote its growth ever upwards over and above all other buds, but those same hormones also represent a form of growth regulation, limitation and control for all of the lateral buds in favour of the Apical bud. Hence we get the variations on the broadly triangular "young" single stemmed tree shape.

Those hormone regulated side branches just grow ever outward and as a result they typically have wide angles of attachment to the stem. Tests have shown that such wide angled forks are relatively strongly attached and are therefore unlikely to fail.

In this way, the Apical bud is the only one that grows consistently upward or towards the light while the remaining branches are cast in a supportive role by not being allowed to compete for upward growth.

So by that simple control, the apical bud is designed to control the resources that the tree can gather, use and control those resources to grow strongly upward into the gap in the canopy and capture the available light.

As a direct result, young trees of most natural species that have evolved in the competitive environment of the primeval woodland, would typically have just one leader while young and as a direct result, have a generally triangular profile. The branch unions to the lateral branches have wide angles of attachment, (and are therefore relatively strongly attached to the tree), and those branches (like the central leader) would generally be straight, just like the trunk, at that point in the trees life.

The image below is a simple form representing the winter profile of the tree that you will recognise as a young tree shape common to many tree species.

It is intended to represent a young Sycamore (Acer pseudoplatanus). In this young tree form and in its original context, (the primeval forest), this young morphology and the upward growth that it is designed to maximise persists until the tree grows up to and through the gap in the canopy to win. The most important races of its life, the first sprint.

Then, at the point at which the tree grows out through the gap in the high canopy something profound occurs that represents the first really significant change in the tree's young life. What happens next is so subtle that it is easily missed.

As the tree emerges into the area above the general height of the surrounding trees it becomes exposed to environmental influences in various ways. Exposure in ways which are new or more extreme, act on the growth tip and apical bud in ways that it is relatively unused to but it is what happens immediately after that I want draw your attention to.

So the tip reaches up above the canopy of the trees surrounding. As it does it becomes exposed to wind or frosts and the full range of adverse occurrences that come with sticking its top shoot out and above the height of the surrounding trees.

The tree has little choice because the growth hormones produced by the Apical bud continue to dictate the mode of growth. It is hormonally compelled to grow ever upward and as it does, its relative exposure increases.

As the relative exposure increases, the growth tip and the apical bud become ever more likely to be damaged or knocked off and eventually, the growth tip with the apical bud is lost. This triggers the first profound change in the structure of the tree.

For the first time and in just one brief moment in its life, there is no Apical bud and therefore no hormones to impose Apical Dominance on all of the lateral branches.

In that same moment the side branches are no longer rigorously controlled and prevented from competing with the briefly missing Apical bud.

The absence of the hormonal controls sets off a profound change in the structure of tree as many side branches have a very brief opportunity to grow in forms that are less rigorously controlled than was the case in the young tree.

In that moment in the life of the tree, the side branches will typically take the opportunity to change direction and grow upwards towards the light or they may fork and divide into two or three small branches and that's the point, without Apical Dominance and Apical control, anything can happen.

The most useful aspect of that for tree care is that because trees create their own structure year on year, the evidence of this event is visible in the trees morphology from then on. It was the shadow or the impression of this event that I first saw in mature trees. That impression intrigued me because even though I did not know how it happened, I had correctly recognised it as the shadow of the young tree preserved in the mature tree.

The image below is just a few months after the apical bud was first lost and the various lateral branches have forked, mostly in conjunction with the new fork in the main stem.

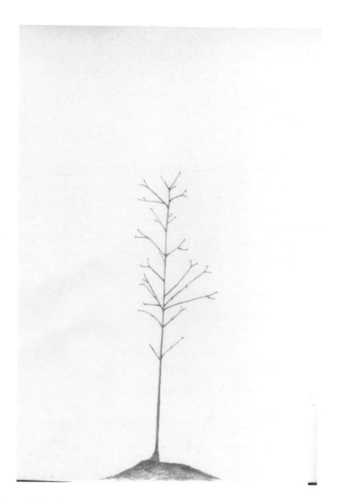

The difference is subtle, but this is the point in the trees life just after it has changed from being an Apically dominant (triangular) form, into a more rounded top form that I hope you come to recognise as the beginnings of the mature, rounded tree shape.

You could say that this is the point in time when the young vigorous upward growth changed into a more mature phase of its life. If trees could, I believe that they would recognise the significance of this event. It is a tree's coming of age so to speak.

Apical dominance is re-established quickly but by now there are numerous Apical buds at the ends of the various branches, each of which establishes Apical control over the parts of the tree that it is connected to and each uses the resources available to it to grow in the particular direction in which any single apical bud, is extending.

Each does that by producing those same growth regulators that allowed the single Apical bud to control the whole young tree but in contrast to the young tree form, there are multiple Apical buds and each therefore just controls it's own branch or part of the tree.

Apical controls are re-established and for a while there is a return to apicallly controlled growth characterised by straight branches with few twists, turns or other distinctive kinds of branch junctions. All lateral branches and leaders will be growing upward or outward towards the light where possible to maximise the trees ability to gather sunlight.

These instances (where Apical dominance is briefly lost), are called "Growth Phase Changes" and the first such growth phase change is the most recognisable and happens when the single Apical bud of the young tree is lost.

Growth phase changes have great significance to the mature tree. They literally change its shape but they also have other greater significance and usefulness to the tree which I will come back to later.

Back to the tree in question, perhaps 24 feet tall by now and broadening its canopy just like the tree in the primeval woodland did. It has grown on for a few years now beyond the first Growth Change.

Apical dominance was re-established with many terminal Apical buds and the growth regimen has carried that growth on in the classically uniform morphology that apical dominance creates. That is, straight branches with few twists and turns.

This next image captures the second growth phase that emerges a few years after the first.

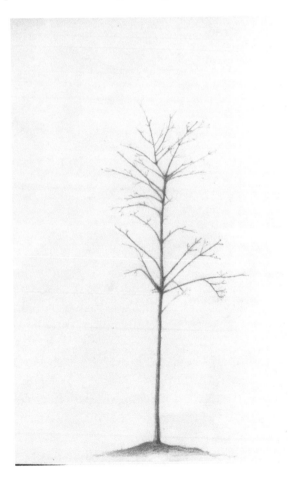

Contrasting to the first, when the single Apical bud was lost, there are numerous apical buds all over the tree and in this change many but not all of those Apical buds are equally affected.

It is a subtle one when it first occurs but it can be seen by the simultaneous forks, twists and turns that occur suddenly at the ends of many of the branches which characterise and record such Growth Phase Change events.

Now I should admit here that while I know that the loss of the single Apical bud affects the whole of the young tree in a profound way, the successive growth phase changes and the circumstances that precipitate them are more difficult to fully understand.

They happen and the evidence of that is held and preserved in the structure of the tree through to maturity but there are many different ways that they can happen. However I have not determined if there is some internal mechanism that precipitates successive growth phase changes as opposed to external event that might cause it or a bit of both.

If it is an external, environmental factor then that event would have to affect the whole tree in one event and happen with predictable regularity because the evidence of it is so widespread.

Conversely, if it is caused by an internal mechanism, what is it? This gave me some headaches for years until I decided to look for the most plausible explanations first, so I was looking for (a theoretical model that most closely followed the rules and fits the growth phase change model that is preserved in the tree structures around us.

Having considered everything, I believe that what may cause successive Growth Phase Changes in temperate climates are mostly either un-seasonal late spring frosts or mid summer drought. Yes there are other processes and cycles that may be involved but there are a couple of front runners as the most likely to cause successive growth phase changes.

Later spring frosts come just as the succulent leaves are emerging and will have an effect primarily on the most exposed, peripheral buds by causing the cells of the newly exposed leaves and flowers to freeze and rupture which effectively destroys the bud just at the point in the growing season that the tree is at its most fragile and delicate.

Mid summer droughts can also stress the tree and cause it to die back from the tips of the branches (the apical buds) so as to make the leaf area smaller which enables the tree to survive the drought and grow on to maturity.

Of course there may be other natural causes including reproductive cycles, pests and certain diseases, but late spring frosts and intense droughts occur with the relative regularity and affect the tree uniformly which mean that they are likely to cause the concentrations of major branch junctions that can be seen preserved in a series of points in time, in the structure of trees.

Crucially, either of these causes are likely to affect the whole tree in the way that is likely to precipitate the growth phase change around the whole trees structure that can bee seen in most mature trees.

So in this way, the tree oscillates between different growth phases, consisting of periods of apical dominance characterised by straight expansive and vigorous growth separated by periodic growth phase changes that allow branches to briefly fork, twist and turn in an amorphous form.

Jargon break – Amorphous (source http://dictionary.reference.com/browse/amorphous)

a·mor·phous

  –adjective

1.

Lacking definite form; having no specific shape; formless: the amorphous clouds.

2.

Of no particular kind or character; indeterminate; having no

pattern or structure; unorganized: an amorphous style; an amorphous personality.

In this simple way the Growth Phase Changes differentiate the structure of the tree and create the familiar forms that we know and love.

The interplay between those two types of growth (growth phases and growth phase changes) actually create the structure that we see in mature trees and by marching back time and imagining the shape that the tree had at each successive growth phase change, you can work out the profile shape that the tree had at each of those stages of its life.

Some Growth Phase Changes are more subtle than others but that would fit very well with the variability of environmental factors being a driving force. Frosts or droughts can be subtle or severe and can even affect only parts of the tree or the whole tree but both affect the emergent, peripheral Apical buds and thereby precipitate these grand changes to the shape of the trees branches.

So the tree grows on, going through a series and succession of events and adversities and as it does, it creates a succession of forks or deviations of direction at the sites of the growth phase changes and at each of those, the number of apical buds increases.

Then there are the un-natural adversities represented by human management of the trees. Any of these things can cause the loss of the apical buds and the consequential brief loss of apical dominance precipitating growth phase changes that I hope you can now begin to see developing in the subject tree images.

In the next image you will see the mature tree, with all of the subtle or not so subtle phased growth changes visible in its structure so that by reviewing the images you can review the events that literally shaped the morphology of the tree.

In that way, you can replay the life of the tree, suddenly understanding as you do, how those structures and the changes that created those structures likely occurred.

Seeing the life history fixed in the tree and understanding it's life as a series of events, all of which have changed the tree and left their mark in it's structures is the first insight that I wanted to reveal to you because in that one leap, you just learned how your tree was constructed over the period of its life as the cumulative result of the nature of the tree and the site specific fluctuations of the weather or other factors, that affected it at various points through its life, changing the course of its life and forming its shape.

That is just an interesting factoid because it is a fact out of context.. It's interesting and nice to be able to read but in and of itself it is not particularly significant to tree management. However, later I will explain what I believe is the real ground breaking importance of that skill and how I firmly believe the ability to read the history of the tree is absolutely central and fundamental to understanding, specifying and providing truly sympathetic tree work. I will also explain why I believe that it is an absolutely essential "client skill" for the well informed tree owner to develop.

For now, have fun with it, review these images and then have a look at any large mature trees around you to see if you can spot these structures in the field.

When you look at different species and different individuals within that species don't be surprised if you have some initial difficulty identifying these features. The species that I have chosen to use for illustrative purposes (Sycamore) just happens to be a species that clearly exhibit these morphological traits in a way that lends itself to illustration and interpretation.

Different species express and exhibit these traits and their growth phase changes subtly differently. It is the differences in each species interpretation and expression of this fundamental organising principle that creates the recognisable characteristics of that species but by just knowing the rules of the morphology game, you can come to understand how your tree interprets those rules.

In fact, understanding the growth phase changes enables you to study the particular species characteristics, the types of forks created at the growth phase changes, the shape of the branches created under apical dominance all of which tend to characterise the morphology of that species.

I include many images of other species and a number of case histories at the end that will provide contrasting examples of how different species exhibit this trait subtly differently.

Then there will be individuals that lost the Apical bud unusually early in their lives. Such trees have narrow or acute forks and co-dominant trunks. What you need to bear in mind is that such trees are simply a different expression of the same fundamental growth rules.

In the case of the tree with a low fork and two stems, it lost its apical bud unusually early in its life for some reason. Then apical dominance was re-established by just two side by side apical buds that went on to grow into the two co-dominant stems until a frost or drought imposed change.

Another thing implicit to this type of growth is the grand changes that it imposes on the shape of the tree. In the young tree all growth is focussed on the apical bud first. This produces the triangular profile of a young tree. At the first growth phase change multiple apical buds are created and so the resources of the tree are divided to create growth in all directions.

At each successive growth phase change more and more apical buds result and so the potential growth of the tree is spread out as those resources are distributed to all of the apical buds. Tip extension will be dramatically different when comparisons are made between an Apical bud on top of a young tree and an Apical bud on the side of a mature tree that has experienced a number of growth phase changes. That is simply because the tree has access to a limited resource of moisture, light and nutrients. So the apparent variations in the relative distance between growth phase changes, as a tree matures are mostly to do with how the tree shares its resources between one or many apical buds.

Of course, what you have seen so far is a virtual tree that has been drawn specifically to illustrate what I am trying to describe and illustrate to. So let me now show you the real tree on which this study is based so that you can identify the point at which the tree first lost its apical bud. Then you will be able to make out the shape that the young tree had at that point as well as the shapes that it had attained at subsequent growth phase changes.

There are at least 4 distinct growth phase changes that are clearly visible in this particular tree and their origins have been highlighted in the preceding illustrations so that you can now review and understand their origins and significance to the development of the morphology of the mature tree. Seeing the mature tree as the culmination of events affecting it through its life, is more important than you might believe.

Chapter 3

Ok, to change the scope of our focus let's look at just one small thing, one small facet of how trees grow because in reality it is a big conundrum that once fully understood, gives a new perspective on how trees grow and dynamically adapt.

Understanding how the growth phase changes benefit the tree is the circumstantial evidence backing this concept because there are certainly tangible benefits that the tree will benefit from including "weak" forms of branch union and in this chapter I will start to illustrate them.

It is those benefits and the strategic genetic advantages that come from them and how they have shaped the genetic evolution of trees, that for me constitute the strongest supporting evidence that my phased growth change model is accurate and truly describes an organising principle of the most successful and numerous woody plant species because of the numerous advantages that the tree enjoys as a result.

To begin to illustrate this, lets us start by focussing closely on one structural phenomena, acutely angled tree branch (and trunk) forks.

Acute Forks have been extensively studied and as a result are widely understood in the Arboriculture industry to be variably weak and therefore are liable to be a point to which the tree will fail in high winds. As a direct result acute forks are considered to be detrimental, disadvantageous and therefore, undesirable for their human owners, but what about the tree?

The reason such forms are weak is because as bark becomes included in the fork as the two branches grow and thicken against each other, the included bark actually prevents bonding of the sinews between the two branches leaving the branches prevented from adopting a strong round form by the proximity of it's neighbour also arising from the acute fork.

I have seen the result of simple pulling tests that suggest that an acute fork can fail at up to approx half of the lateral loading that would be required to make a straight trunk or branch of similar dimensions fail. Tests aside anecdotal evidence suggests to me that acute forks fail whenever a strong gusting or roaring wind comes through because I have seen many hundreds that have failed in high or even just in moderately gusting winds.

That has made acute forks the subject of many an Arboricultural report as a significant defect simply because they represent a clear and tangible risk of failure in high winds. Of course any thing or person that is beneath the part of the tree that such a failure is likely to liberate so that it can fall, would be at risk from the branch falling onto it, him or her.

Consequentially, acute angled forks are not liked or appreciated by risk averse humans and for entirely understandable reasons. We don't like branches and tree trunks falling into our gardens, but what about trees? Given the human perspective, it is hard to see weak structural features as the strategic design benefits that they are.

For contrast with trees, we humans have evolved from Apes to Homo Sapiens in about 100th of the time (about 5 million years), that trees have been evolving.

Therefore considering that we have evolved from Ape like bipeds to humans in that relatively short time, as a result of trees 500 million year long evolutionary path I would have expected "defects" like acute forks, to have been mostly lost from highly evolved trees and consigned to the fossil records. That is however, only if acute forks truly were disadvantageous to the likely survival of an individual tree and through the individual, disadvantageous to the survival of the species.

Recognising the benefits contained in the adversity that acute forks represent shows how trees turn the adversity that weak branch forks represent, into an opportunity.

Evolution would not have favoured a truly defective organism to persist for long and the fact that acute or otherwise less strong forks occur in almost all tree species and across even most families of trees, should make us re-appraise their significance so that we can define their true "Value" to the tree and then again, their value to tree owners too because it is that relationship that needs re-orienting.

Jargon break – Value

The term "Value" can be interpreted as "the anticipation of future benefit" (source Scott Cullen in relation to the Guide For Plant Appraisal and Valuation workshops that he conducted for the Consulting Arborist Society when I was chairperson of that organisation from 2002 to 2009).

Acute forks with included bark are the extreme, the weakest form of branch union.

Narrow forks are less relatively weak than acute forks and wide forks are generally even stronger than narrow forks, so the degree of relative weakness goes up with the relative narrowness or the "acuteness" of the fork as a general rule.

So what possible Value can the tree derive from these forks? What is the anticipated future benefit that trees derive from developing acute and narrow forks within their structure? Then, why do these features persist through the generations because it is that that persistence demonstrates that they are a benefit to the species more than anything else?

Well perhaps it has something to do with the fact that variable fork morphology, producing forks that have variable abilities to withstand the actions of changeable wind strengths acting on it, creates a structure that can change and fail, progressively?

What I am saying is that trees, having had 500 million years to evolve into the forms that we see today, carry a persistent defect.

That defect, (variable strength branch unions ranging from weak to strong), is extremely widespread across species and whole families of trees.

In fact it is widespread across most families of trees and bear in mind that some of the Families of trees evolved on isolated land masses separated by geological time spans. Even so, most trees carry this "defect".

That means just one thing.   Acute Forks are not defects at all, (to the tree).

As Acute Forks evidently do not represent a defect to the tree, they have to be a benefit.

In fact, to persist so widely distributed amongst the tree species, they must be a fundamental benefit and part of a wider strategy that will enable the tree to survive individual energetic climactic events by preparing certain branches for partial failure back to the weak fork so that the bulk of the mature tree is likely to survive energetic but short lived storms.

So what is the Value, in other words, what is "the future benefit" that trees can expect to get by having narrow or even acute forks built into their structures?

Well, there are some other concepts to introduce before I fully illustrate that issue but in the broadest sense, variable strength tree forks give a tree dynamic adaptability in direct response to fluctuating climate and even unusually energetic individual events.

Now of course trees are static creatures so the "dynamic" aspect might more properly be described as "passive dynamic adaptability" because the tree prepares itself to passively and progressively fail from the edge inwards and that has a profound effect on the dynamic response of the tree to wind which is the subject of the next chapter.

The next image shows the most dangerous kind of tree fork and it is worth understanding exactly why it is so likely to fail.

Firstly, it is a fork on the trunk and rising from it are two, co-dominant stems.

Because they are co-dominant, both having their own apical buds both compete with each other for upward growth rather than just competing with the trees around.

Because both leaders have the same resources they grow at the same rate.

Because they set off at the same point in time, neither can outgrow the other and they remain locked in a battle for growth that neither can win.

The results of such a co-dominant morphology is strong competition between the two or more stems which inevitably produces strong upward growth.

That strong upward (or outward) growth, places ever greater structural demands on the timber at the fork which is coincidentally the point in the trees structure that it is least able to resist those forces.

Because the two leaders rise so closely to each other, as they grow against one another bark becomes embedded and included in the fork and this prevents the timber of the two leaders from binding properly with each other.

The final problem comes when wind acts on the two or more leaders.

As they move independently of each other, the forces acting on each ding branch are focussed in the acute fork as the branches move against one another in an action similar to the way that scissors work so that the fork experiences shear forces as the leaders move away from each other, or compression leverage as they move towards one another.

Those forces act on the branches causing them to bend and sway in a way that can lead to a crack propagating down the trunk (or major structural branch), from the base of the acute fork. Cracks can result that propagate down from the fork, further weakening the fork and eventually resulting in one of the leaders falling.

The cumulating factors are subtle, but once you understand the forces and conflicts involved, such defects are relatively easy to spot.

Bear in mind as you look at your own trees in search of such defects, that in my industry we don't tend to risk rate trees surprising as that may sound. In fact Arborists tend to risk rate targets (things that parts of a defective tree might land on). Target rating takes into account the relative exposure of the target.

So a tree with an acute fork that has a propagating crack that is over a playground or road will have an appropriately high "target rating" but if the same tree is next to a footpath running through a field, then passers by will be so briefly and so seldom in the target area that the risk would be calculated to be much lower. I mention this so that readers might avoid overreacting to perceived risks. If in doubt and assessing the significance of risks is a difficult balance to find, ask your local tree care expert for their opinion.

In the example on the next page, it's the crack beneath that makes this such an imminently latent defect. Just add the wrong gust of wind and this type of latent defect can become an incident.

Chapter 4

Let's change the scope of our focus back to broad principles and another specific area of my experimentation and research – Resonance Frequencies in organic structures.

It is a widely accepted fact that everything resonates at some frequency or other and it is both a familiar thing (musical instruments for example) and yet is also a very complicated subject. As jargon, (I would suggest that its essential jargon), its worth an explanation.

Resonance (source http://hyperphysics.phy-astr.gsu.edu/hbase/sound/reson.html)

In sound applications, a resonant frequency is a natural frequency of vibration determined by the physical parameters of the vibrating object. This same basic idea of physically determined natural frequencies applies throughout physics in mechanics, electricity and magnetism, and even throughout the realm of modern physics.

1. *It is easy to get an object to vibrate at its resonant frequencies, hard to get it to vibrate at other frequencies.*
2. *A vibrating object will pick out its resonant frequencies from a complex excitation and vibrate at those frequencies, essentially "filtering out" other frequencies present in the excitation.*
3. *3. Most vibrating objects have multiple resonant frequencies*

What set me off down the path of researching Resonance Frequencies, were two particular experiences that happened to me in a tree. One happened just once and I could so easily have missed it, the other happened many times and puzzled me each time it did.

The single experience was simply a tingle that I felt in the palm of my hand that I could so easily have missed entirely.

What pre-disposed me to see something significant in resonances in trees were the earlier experiences climbing trees in windy conditions. Those experiences occurred in the pit of my stomach. That feeling was simply motion sickness resulting from my climbing up a relatively thin tree combined with the effect that my moving my mass up that tree had on the resonance frequency of that tree or branch.

I could so easily have missed the significance of these phenomena altogether but instead they set me off on another intriguing voyage of discovery into the material properties of timber in its natural form in the living tree.

What I discovered through testing and further research was that trees have either a simple resonance frequency or a series of resonance frequencies that are different and distinct to each other. So a simple single stem trees usually have a dominant single resonance frequency whereas more complicated tree structures have different parts that all have a range of distinct resonances, or in other words, a resonance spectrum.

The interesting bit that really caught my attention was that the resonance frequencies that I experienced and then measured were constants even when different strength gusts of wind were acting on the trees that I was measuring.

It is unusual to find a measurable constant in an organic science so I was intrigued.

Now let me say up front that the tests that I did were done on tall single stemmed trees. In such forms the tree has a rather obvious dominant single resonance frequency that it is possible to assess and measure using visual observations and a stop watch. Let me also reveal that I am in process of designing a device that will "read" the resonance spectrum of trees which are not simple single stem examples.

When I use the term resonance frequency with regard to trees I mean one very obvious expression of it. When a tree is deflected by a gust of wind it bends then when the gust has passed it sways back through its start point to a point of maximum recovery before swaying back through the start point again.

That motion continues as the tree sways back and to, getting smaller in amplitude through each sway although the swaying motions still take the same amount of time to complete each successive cycle. That is the constant that I am referring to, the resonant frequency.

Through this swaying motion the tree transfers some of the windload down through its branches, trunk and roots to be dissipated into the mass of soil to which the roots are connected but most is lost through friction between the branches, twigs and (in summer) the leaves and the air. Of course those transferred windloads can cause problems for lightweight or brittle structures built onto the soils into which the windloads are ultimately transferred and thereby dissipated, but that is another issue that I will explore in a later book.

That movement or the number of seconds that it takes to complete one swaying cycle is what I call the resonance frequency of the tree. So that you can imagine it as it happened in my tests, I measured such resonance frequency cycles which took as long as four and a half seconds to complete.

Because the air that moved the tree also provides damping through simple wind resistance, these oscillations do not persist for many cycles but in the first or second cycles, it does provide a measurable phenomenon that you can capture in the field or sense in the motion sensors in your middle ear and even your stomach.

What I discovered when I did this was what I initially presumed to be just another trivial pursuits factoid, that trees resonate. The significance of that discovery were not immediately apparent to me, however It would emerge that there was a link between the weak forks by way of one complicated mathematical model and another ridiculously simple mathematical equation and the growth phase changes described in Chapter 2.

Don't worry, this will knit together well by the end and in fact knitting the loose ends is what has taken such a long time for me to complete. Back to the story…

In an organic science, it is unusual to find constants but when I did realise that I had discovered one, I also realised that it must be significant in some way and as a result I redoubled my efforts to find out why and to determine what could be learned from my findings, if anything.

What I discovered through wider research was this…. In exactly the same way that the regular motion of a metronome is dictated by the position of the moveable weight (mass) along its length and the elastic properties of its mounting point, the period of the swaying motions of a tree are dictated by the position of it's centre of gravity (mass) along it's length and the relative flexibility of the timber.

As the period that a given tree takes to go through one cycle is fixed by the parameters of the trees size, shape and form, it follows that the only implications of higher strength gusts acting on the tree, is an increase in the amplitude (the extent) of the swaying motion and an increase in the relative speeds of that movements back and forth following a gust.

To draw a musical analogy with a stringed instrument, the pitch of the note stays the same, but the amplitude of the movements of the string (the volume that we hear) goes up. Pluck a string harder, the sound gets louder but the resonance frequency (the pitch) does not change. The same principle applies to the swaying motion of trees.

So small gusts produce gentle and relatively slow moving swaying motions, whereas strong gusts produce larger, more vigorous movements and higher speeds of movement at the swaying tips of the branches.

The constant, which is the resonance frequency, is the length of time that these small or large swaying motions take to complete a cycle and that is the constant that I believe is so significant and practically useful to anybody interested in trees.

I believe that the Resonance Frequency of a tree is an alternative and measurable "expression" of the morphology of that tree which has itself been changed and moulded by its environment. It is a measurable phenomenon that represents in one simple number, the tree's site specific morphological adaptation.

Resonance is not the only story because trees also use its exact opposite "dissonance".

Jargon break "Dissonance" (Latin dis-, "apart" + sonare, "to sound"),

Where different portions of the tree end up having different parts broken off in high winds as a natural part of the ageing process, the different branches end up resonating at different frequencies. The key phrase here is different portions, because dissonance is a characteristic of trees with lots of mature branches. In other words, mature trees, so it is a time of life thing.

The net result of these dissonant and distinct resonance frequencies in more mature tree forms is that those different frequencies do not necessarily dynamically amplify each other. In fact the movement of dissonant parts of a tree can be described as "mass damping" against each other in such a way that their movements partially negate each other so that the full force of a wind gust might be partially damped out before the forces reach the lower trunk.

That means that the net resulting forces that get transferred down the trunk and roots into the surrounding soil are modified and reduced somewhat by the dissonance and consequential mass damping that occur in mature trees.

The way that different parts of the tree resonate at different frequencies and thereby partially cancel each other out has rather obvious benefits to those mature trees.

Measurements taken in the field suggest that young single stemmed trees or tall single stemmed forest grown trees have a single or at least a clearly overwhelmingly dominant resonance frequency.

Mature trees where different parts of the tree have been changed by occasional branch failures have some degree of dissonance between differently resonating parts which cancels out the effects on the tree as a whole by mass damping but here again, if a mature tree has a dominant resonant mass then it will clearly resonate like a young tree, and a single dominant resonance frequency that can easily be measured.

In early maturity there will usually still be one dominant resonance frequency relating to the movement of the largest portion of the tree that sways.

As an example of how ignoring mass damping can cause catastrophic failure, I used to manage the trees for a country estate. Some time before they engaged me, there had been a huge grown out Beech pollard many hundreds of years old and in a prominent position.

Historical records showed that it had been successively lopped at about 15 feet when farming practice required the facility to cut the resulting small branches to feed animals in times of drought but that particular practice had stopped nearly 200 years before and the tree had been left to grow since that time. It was by all accounts a truly massive old tree that had significant aesthetic impact.

Since pollarding had ceased 200 years ago the canopy had grown to be formed by massive multiple co-dominant stems rising from the original pollard point.

Taking the advice that had been offered to him, the landowner agreed to have that Beech comprehensively braced with wire braces. This was conceived as a way to make catastrophic failure less likely so as to preserve the tree, perhaps even for another 200 years.

That was no small undertaking on such a huge old tree with so many leaders but the job was completed with many braces inter-connecting the many and various leaders like a spiders web. As a result of the extensive work, the tree was assumed to have a better chance of not loosing one of the multiple leaders, than it had before.

The upshot of all this was that within 2 weeks, that tree failed from the base in strong, (but certainly not "very strong"), winds.

I don't read too much into this, after all, the tree could have been ready to fall in that particular wind on that day anyway.

However it does seem to have poignant significance because the wind strength on the day it failed was not unusual to the tree and while this is speculation on my part, I am of the opinion that the reason that tree failed at that time is simply that by cross bracing the various leaders in many ways, the bracing had made all of the different leading branches act as one. It was probably the first time in well over 200 years that that was the case.

The bracing did two things in my opinion. It moved the crisis point down to a point below the previous weakest part of the tree, (which would have been the pollard point) and it stopped the different leaders from having their own distinct resonance frequencies so it prevented dissonance and consequential mass damping.

The bracing meant that different parts of the tree quite suddenly stopped swaying at different speeds so that the whole tree had one single resonance frequency which removed the beneficial mass damping effect and transferred the resulting loadings in total, down into the trunk and roots which is the point at which the tree promptly failed in the next strong wind which, as I said, happened just a few weeks later.

Trees are self adapting structures but the sudden absence of mass damping sent the forces acting on the canopy down to the roots without the beneficial reduction in the overall forces through dissonant mass damping. The roots, which had become adapted to the forces that used to be transferred down through them after mass damping, proved up-prepared for the larger transferred wind loads coming down from the comprehensively braced canopy and the total failure resulted in the complete loss of the tree.

As a result of this case I advise people think many times over before bracing any tree because it changes the way trees work dynamically in wind in a fundamental way. By doing so bracing a large old and complicated tree can actually make the failure of the tree much more likely.

Another reason not to brace a tree is because it is tacit recognition that a weakness exists in the tree. Admitting that there is a weakness and a risk is one thing. Addressing that risk in a way that is ineffective by design and could be argued that it makes a disaster more likely, is not going to be something that can be easily defended in court if somebody was unlucky enough to be injured or killed by the subsequent failure of that tree.

Personally I never advise bracing for these reasons but also because bracing is not how trees typically deal with such issues. I prefer a different solution. Co-incidentally the solution that I use is the same solution that 500 million years of evolution has evolved in trees.

Natural dissonance is the main reason that I do not advocate bracing trees because bracing compromises dissonance and can (as it seemed with the Beech in my example) eliminate beneficial dissonance. Bracing also makes all parts of the tree act together which in turn moves the crisis point (the point at which the tree is most likely to fail), down into the lower trunk or roots in a way which the tree will not be used to.

Trees don't typically brace themselves, it can happen by grafting, but it is unusual. Trees "reduce" structural stress in a controlled way. Understanding and appreciating the elegance of the tree's own evolutionary designed strategy to reduce and manage stresses on its structure is the main focus of this book.

Anyway, to contrast with dissonance, tall trees or young trees with a single stem can have one simple dominant resonance frequency.

I measured such single stemmed trees with resonance frequencies of 3, 4 or more seconds. That is a long period and illustrates the magnitude of forces acting through tall, mature trees where there may be tens or even hundreds of tons of mass in motion.

Such trees with long resonance frequencies have to be at risk of dynamic amplification by successive gusts of wind. That is because the longer they take to go through one cycle means that the next gust is ever more likely to arrive in time to dynamically amplify the swaying movement.

Dynamic amplification of the sway would happen if the tree, at the fullest extent of it's recovery after being deflected by a gust, were to be hit at around that moment by another gust. The consequence of such an event is that the forces loaded into the tree, the tension that pulls the tree back though the centre point of its motion becomes added to the force exerted on the tree by the next gust of wind.

The tension in the tree pulling the mass back through its start point is added to the force in the gust of wind pushing the tree again and those two forces are combined in such a way that although neither of the successive gusts were strong enough to cause failure, the power contained in both gusts, becomes linked by the swaying of the tree so that the power in the second gust is added to the residual power from the first gust that set the tree swaying.

Another example of this phenomenon occurs in tall buildings that are being designed for earthquake zones. Such buildings are now designed so that they do not resonate at frequencies that match (or are harmonic multiples of) the natural likely frequencies of seismic waves travelling through the earth and/or they have free moving masses (sometimes liquid) to mass damp the swaying motion.

By designing those building to resonate at frequencies that are not dynamically amplified by the range of natural frequencies shaking the ground in an earthquake, the building just has to survive the energy in each seismic wave rather than having those successive seismic waves add their energy to each other within the structure of the building.

I am sure that everybody has seen the film footage of the Tacoma Narrows Bridge disaster that happened in November 1940 . "Galloping Gertie" was the bridge's given name, coined by the onlookers. http://www.youtube.com/watch?v=3mclp9QmCGs.

Also, see this http://www.youtube.com/watch?v=xlOS_31Ubdo&NR=1 to see how small scale movements can dynamically amplify much larger structures if the small movements excite that structure in synchronicity with the resonance frequency of the large structure.

Then look at this YouTube clip to see resonance in action the final phase of this animation illustrates mass damping (similarly to how it occurs in trees) better than any written explanation that I could offer.
http://www.youtube.com/watch?v=PSjchBpKK9U&feature=related.

After that, if you have found the previous links interesting, try Schumann waves at this link http://www.youtube.com/watch?v=LbMVPkMoxro.

The Tacoma narrows bridge had flat sides and as a result, when wind came up the valley that the bridge spanned at just the right (or wrong speed, which was anything over 35mph), the bridge shed vortices above and then below the deck. Unfortunately the resonance frequency of the bridge was dynamically amplified by the frequency with which those vortices went successively over and then under the bridge causing oscillations that were dynamically amplified until the whole structure failed.

Where trees are concerned, when the tree bends as the gust hits, then recovers by swaying back in the direction that the gust came from, the tree is at risk of dynamic amplification if another gust hits at the moment of its fullest recovery. If it is hit at that moment the forces stored in the trunk are added to the force that the second gust places on the tree and those two forces acting together, dynamically amplify the severity of the swaying motion beyond what the wind strength could achieve on its own in one gust.

What that means is that the longer the resonance frequency, the more likely that a subsequent gust of wind will occur at a frequency that can dynamically amplify the extent of the forces acting through the tree trunk so that those combined forces can exceed the structures that the tree has developed in the gradual self adaptive process of normal growth.

The subject of Resonance Frequencies in organic structures is huge and this is just a snapshot introduction to illustrate some implications of it. It is something that I will expand on significantly in the next books in this series and it is a subject that I think has the potential to provide some wonderfully insightful and even useful tools for tree owners, Arboriculturists and tree officers alike.

For now however, I hope that the very brief introduction that this represents has given you some idea of the forces and the phenomenon involved because it is of direct relevance to this book and your trees as I will show you.

The lessons of Tacoma Narrows Bridge and the design of modern earthquake resistant buildings for tree owners is that resonance frequencies in organic structures are a phenomenon that is worth a bit of research and understanding.

The fact that we don't build trees is the most significant difference, but we can come to a more profound understanding and interact with trees more harmoniously by considering just how they have been designed by evolution designing strategies to enable trees to dynamically change their shape and by changing their shape, change how they react to and dissipate forces from wind by swaying in the wind.

Further to that, I believe that it is possible to actually "tune" (or bearing in mind the benefits of different parts having different resonance frequencies, perhaps I should say "detune") a tree. That is, to subtly adjust the resonance frequency of the whole tree or portions of that tree if it has a range of resonances in its various parts and by doing so, provide measurable proof of the simple mechanical advantage that you can give the tree.

If you were swinging around a large tree in a harness in windy conditions (and I really do recommend that you do, if only once), you would feel it for yourself as a feeling in the pit of your stomach. The feeling intensifies as you get further up a tall ascending branch or in a slender but tall tree and its something akin to travel sickness, (at least it is to me) so that I feel uneasy, slightly queasy almost. The higher I would go, the worse it got but it was not the height that affected me.

The higher I went, the more my body mass changed the relationship between the trees height and the distribution of that mass. By climbing ever higher therefore I was lengthening the resonance frequency and it was sensing that change, that I believe produced the effect that I experienced.

The image above was taken at the City of London Cemetery during the clear up after the storm of 1987. 210 acres of chaos (when we arrived). This project involving the removal of hundreds of fallen trees from amongst tight packed marble monuments and the further restoration of many hundreds of wind damaged but still standing trees, gave me some of the insights that have since developed into this book. That job represented an unusual opportunity to map the destruction across the whole 210 acre site in the process dealing with lines of same species, same aged trees that had been severely to lightly damaged.

I can't emphasise enough how that job exposed me to how trees deal with adversity and over the following years I also saw how they recover from it.

Anyway, when I first used to get that uneasy feeling very early in my career I would remove a small branch and as I did that, the feeling would subside or change slightly, get better for sure and as I removed more small side branches, the feeling continued improving.

There is another animal that has gained an unrivalled sense of resonance frequencies and how to practically use them because they use them to move around their forest home. That animal is of course, the Orang-utan.

University of Liverpool School of Biomedical Sciences has published a very interesting piece about how Orang-utans (which are the largest arboreal ape) use resonance and dissonance that you can read here http://www.sciencedaily.com/releases/2009/07/090727191908.htm.

Or http://www.telegraph.co.uk/earth/wildlife/9105864/King-of-the-swingers-how-orang-utans-are-like-free-runners.html

I believe however that I have identified another way that Orang-utans use and perhaps abuse the material properties of the trees they live in to move from tree to tree.

I am an avid viewer of wildlife documentaries and like everybody I suspect that we all watch those produced by David Attenborough and the BBC with particular interest for the insightful commentary and the stunning visual impact of the sequences that their film crews have captured.

It was just such a sequence that caught my imagination. It was showing a family group including large adults moving through the canopy. I watched as a large individual moved carefully towards the top of a relatively thin branch. As the animal reached higher its upward movement slowed then stopped as the sounds of sinews snapping in the branch accompanied the gradual and progressive failure of the branch which allowed the Orang-utan to swing towards the adjacent tree that it was trying to reach.

That sequence reminded me of exactly the same feeling that I had had as I edged along relatively narrow or extended branches. As mentioned, I believe that I was sensing the gradually extending resonance frequency as my mass moved along the branch and the sequence showing the Orangutans reminded me of the few times that I accidentally moved my mass to a point that the branch could not sustain it.

Remembering that as I watched transfixed, I also remembered that the feeling that I got as the branch on which I was climbing started to fail. That sensation subsided if I moved my mass by a very small amount back down the branch and I am left with the feeling that I could find that point at which the branch started to fail, exactly as an Orang-utan does, just by how it feels. Of course, it goes without saying that I would not ever try to use that as the Orang-utan does without also having a rope attached to a part of the tree that is not likely to fail but here again is another example of how our bodies have a range of senses that are there to help us to use and move safely through our environment.

YouTube videos showing Orang-utans using resonance to move through the canopy include http://www.youtube.com/watch?v=DQh3MEdU0sw   and http://www.youtube.com/watch?v=HgZT5Xr3vkM.pdf (you can find these links and others in the resources section on the TreeMorphogenesis.com website).

In the first of the two sequences above the Orang-utan moves from one branch to a thinner one. Note as you watch, just how long the resonance frequency of the branch gets as it is deflected but still the animal can not reach. Then, it finally moves it's weight up a very short distance before that movement causes the branch to start to fail and bend in a way that if the animal didn't grab the adjacent tree, the branch on which it was swinging would not have recovered and would probably have snapped.

In the second sequence it starts with a wonderful scene where a young one is swinging back and to on a thin tree. It is subtle and easily missed but as the tree swings to the right, the animal straightens its legs and adjusts its hand hold in such a way that it moves its mass up by a very small amount which lengthens the extent of the sway. That adjustment is all that is necessary to deflect the tree so that it can grab the vine that it is aiming for.

Both of these examples show just how Orang-utans are acutely aware of the material properties of the trees. Orang-utans are amazing and we share 97% of our Genes with them (or in my case, perhaps 97.1%).

So what the University of Liverpool School of Biomedical Sciences articles that I refer to in the previous page miss entirely, is that Orang-utans (like Arborists) use senses to assess exactly at what point a part of the tree on which they are climbing stops resonating and starts to fail, albeit fail in a predictable and useful way.

From the incidents that I remember where branches that I was climbing, failed under my weight, the point just before a branch starts to fail is recognisable because the branch becomes what I can only describe as quite simply "too still". Of course, I was wearing a harness and was tied to the tree. Even so, I never managed to judge the point at which the branch started to fail with anything like the skill and accuracy that Orang-utans can and as I result, I found it impossible to retain my dignity in such incidents. The raucous laughter of my team would always drive home the humiliation and the lesson.

At the point the branch is about to fail the feeling is that almost any movement could set up swaying that will overcome the strength of the tree. Orang-utans have simply taken their sensitivity of feeling to its limits so that they abuse the tree structures in a measured and predictable way, almost breaking the trees but getting away with it through the acute sensitivity of their "feel" for the material properties of the timber of the particular species of tree in which they are climbing.

While I got a glimpse of this phenomenon in my clumsy movements around tree canopies, it was enough for me to recognise the senses that Orangutans use while they abuse the trees that they are passing through.

It was considering and exploring the significance of that feeling that led me indirectly to discovering the significance of resonance frequencies for myself.

When designing maintenance for a tree, it is important that the tree retains some natural flexibility whereby it still sustains mechanical loadings that test its structure and by doing so actually force it to adapt its structure and grow. As a result for sympathetic tree pruning I am advocating only light pruning regimes (5-20% typically).

Always remember that trees are self adaptive structures and that they grow in direct response to structural stresses. Then in stormy weather they can reduce the load by shedding branches to naturally occurring forks at the growth phase changes thereby reducing structural loadings which help avoid the whole tree failing.

Each successive simulated wind pruning reduces the loading on the trunk, making a tree affected in this way, less likely to fail in all but a 100 year storm unless some other degenerative process or simply, if extraordinary wind strengths are involved.

So if you want to live harmoniously with trees for whatever reasons are important to you, then you are most welcome to use "Reduction Via Thinning" and you will make a difference. Trees certainly need you to make that difference believe me but I am a bit more pragmatic, after all, I sell solutions.

What I am focussing on here are (hopefully) well observed and described insights that give a tree owner (or somebody working with trees), some new ways to look at, see and now feel trees as well and if you are lucky enough to be an arborist, sense their resonance frequency as you climb and note the changes that occur in the tree as you climb higher.

Climbers note as you ascend, how it feels as the tree sways and also notice if feelings of anxiety increase as you move your weight higher. Then remove a small side branch or two or move back down just a few inches and see if that changes the feelings you experience. If they do, you probably just sensed the relationship between mass and the structure of the tree in terms of how it affects the resonance frequency of the tree. You probably also got a glimpse of how sensitive Orang-utans are to resonance frequencies.

These sensory phenomenon help the owner and the arborist to better understand the multi sensory experience that is climbing in a tree. They also illustrate and communicate just what a wonderful thing tall tree climbing is as your body weight changes the mass displacement and changes the resonance frequency in a way that you feel and experience in the pit of your stomach.

I strongly urge each and every one of you to get equipped and trained to the appropriate standards of Health & Safety so that you can experience these things for yourself. Arborists sense these things all the time and most probably dismiss them but they are crucially important in the understanding, study and observation of trees.

So armed with the significance of that new sense and the way to use it, an Arborist applying a Simulated Wind Pruning by application of a light Reduction Via Thinning is "tuning" the tree to a state of resonance frequency that "feels" safer. Not spiritual, not theoretical but actually sense and experience the difference in the pit of your stomach.

As an aside, my first website, www.Arbornauts.com was set up in 1995. "Arbornauts" the word that I created for the domain, comprises Arbor, (tree) and Nauts, (people who sail in). So Arbornauts literally means "people who sail in trees" (or at least, to me it does).

While the word has also since become used to collectively describe the ecological researchers exploring the high canopy of rainforests and the like, the word has very special meaning for me.

I can only describe the meaning in this way. If you are an Arborist and you have ever been high up in a tree when wind has been gusting or blowing a gale, you will know exactly what that meaning is. It is literally a feeling in the pit of your stomach. It's scary and yet exhilarating all at the same time. It's a barrage on your senses and well worth the risk. If that idea has real meaning and appeal for you, you are probably an Arbornaut too.

When your whole world is in motion and that motion seems to be very close to that of a tall ship that is being battered by a storm, you will understand Arbornauts (people who sail in trees) completely and intimately. You will also feel very small and fragile.

One final thing about resonance frequencies in trees and it is the "Law Of Diminishing Returns" because I believe that it applies here.

I have found by measuring trees that I have pruned and then testing those results in a mathematical model that there is a strange relationship between the two.

This is something that I will expand on in following books but for now it is important to appreciate that if my findings are correct, then the greatest relative raising of the resonance frequency of a tree might come from the lightest pruning regimes.

I should admit that I do not have enough raw data to confirm my early findings but the data that I have suggests that as little as 5-10% Reduction Via Thinning will raise the resonance frequency by 20-25%. Beyond such light pruning percentages, the relative effect on raising the resonance frequency, seems to be progressively less and less.

This suggests that the greatest benefits can be enjoyed for the lightest pruning regimes and the lightest pruning regimes coincidentally preserve the bulk of the leaf area which in turn, produces the carbohydrates and sugars that are the fuels for growth, defence and further morphological adaptation.

Light pruning regimes are therefore the most beneficial for the tree owner because while the tree can be shown to be measurably less likely to fail in wind (demonstrated by the raising of the resonance frequency), it will also be in an overall condition that will enable it to recover quickly from the pruning and carry on growing and effectively defending itself.

For all of these reasons therefore, I would not usually do Reduction Via Thinning of over 25% of the foliage bearing branches and usually, it is limited to a lot less.

500 million years of tree evolution seems to me to have produced an organism that is designed to grow too close to its potential size given the material properties of the timber and the relative environmental exposure of the location.

Then when energetic and wildly variable climactic events happen and cause damage to the tree, that evolution and the growth phase change differentiated structure (that is one outcome of that evolution), is what facilitates wind pruning.

It is truly efficient because the tree does nothing apart from prepare for such events using the experience contained in the fact that previous generations benefited from the relative variability of the strength of the major branch unions concentrated around the growth phase changes.

> **Growth Phase Changes therefore represent the fundamental organising principle that I believe is the highly evolved survival strategy that benefits the species that have evolved to use it, to the detriment of those that do not.**

Then when peripherally pruned in this natural and somewhat random way, the tree is dynamically changed in the most significant way so that even the smallest reduction in the peripheral mass dramatically reduces structural stresses through the main structure of the tree.

That is a truly elegant system that tree owners and Arborists working on their trees, need to hold in their minds. Save money AND have better trees by understanding them in this particular way.

> **Wind prunes trees in a predictable but brutal way. Arborists who try to simulate wind pruning leave smaller, neater, (cut rather than ripped) wounds that heal quicker. They can decide exactly which growth phase change to use for the final cut rather than always ripping back to the weakest fork, in that way preserving the aesthetic appeal and even the character of the tree.**

> **For these reasons I am inclined to believe that Reduction Via Thinning could actually be more sympathetic to trees even than natural wind pruning and certainly produces more predictable results.**

> **Any tree work that can realistically be described as "more sympathetic than nature itself" is surely a service that people should aspire to providing if you are an Arborist, or utilise and benefit from, if you are a tree owner.**

Here is an absolutely huge Horse Chestnut that I applied a light Reduction Via Thinning to some 8-10 years ago. I hope you can hardly tell it has been pruned.

The image of the same tree (below) is included simply to remind you just how bad the alternative to sympathetic tree care can be.

Hey don't get me wrong, it will sprout with many small foliage bearing branches looking for all the world like a bog brush in winter. It will do that so that it regenerates the leaves lost from the ends of all the branches so that it survives but the natural flow of the larger branches down to the smaller leaf bearing twigs is gone and the poor branch structure that will result will probably require even more work.

You might think this looks fine. All I can say is that leaves hide many things and that before this last pruning regime, this 100' landmark tree was absolutely stunning whereas now in summer or winter, to me it just looks "wrong" compared to how it looked before.

Chapter 5

Cutting to the chase now, I think it's time we looked at the pruning specification that originated in 1988 and then gradually evolved from the inclusion of all this research with an explanation, referring to the things that I have revealed so far, so that you can see where they fit in.

The simple, short specification for "Reduction Via Thinning" is defined like this....

"RVT - Reduction Via Thinning, is a process involving the removal of a small number of primary foliage bearing branches which are carefully removed back to natural pruning points that occur within the canopy of the tree. The effect is to subtly reduce and thin the canopy which reduces wind resistance and gives the roots trunk and structural branches a simple mechanical advantage.
That is all achieved while retaining the shape, functionality and, most importantly, the character of the tree.
By concentrating on and being limited to the removal of small percentages of the peripheral foliage bearing branches, this specification mimics the way a tree allows its branches to progressively fail in high wind which is itself an integral part of the gradual ageing process.
We usually express "RVT" as a percentage of foliage (typically between 5 and 20%) . In this case   %." (© Reduction Via Thinning by David Lloyd-Jones 1995)

That specification has been frequently copied and yet remains the least understood tree pruning specification on the market. High time therefore I finally explain what it really means which is after all, the key purpose of this book.

The insights from Chapter 2, 3 and Chapter 4 need to be pulled together to fully explain Reduction Via Thinning because it is a series of suppositions that feel right in and of themselves and also cumulatively because they are all interconnected and complimentary.

The shapes that trees make growing through their lives, the strategic weaknesses that are build in to the growth phase changes and the way that the loss of branches from those weak forks also changes the resonance frequencies of the whole tree in a dramatic way, those things are all interconnected by design and by evolution.

The "primary foliage bearing branches" are the most extended in every direction so they would also be likely to be the most exposed and consequently, will experience the greatest wind loadings. They also represent the most peripheral mass of the tree.

In pruning an assessed number of those primary branches back to one of the variable strength branch unions originating in a growth phase change, the trees peripheral mass is reduced slightly which moves the centre of mass down slightly and therefore, like a Metronome, this reduces the amount of time the tree takes to sway and recover from being hit by a gust of wind. In other words, it raises the trees resonance frequency.

Then trees being self optimising structures the structural elements remaining will have become over-specified by the removal of even a small portion of its peripheral load. My own tests show that removal of some peripheral mass will raise the resonance frequency by a significant amount that is greater than the simple % of foliage removed would lead you to expect.

The result is subtle, removing only small portions of the whole canopy, thinning it and reducing its overall size slightly.

Because it creates differences between them, structural branches get dissonant resonance frequencies which is a healthy state whereby their individual movements and different swaying cycles of the different resonant components of the tree will tend to cancel each other out to some degree by mass damping their movement against each other before those collective wind loadings are finally transferred further down to the trunk and roots before being dissipated into the surrounding soil.

Then, as the centre of gravity will have moved down slightly, the resonance frequency of the whole tree will have shortened slightly as well.

Then additionally, the self optimised structural elements of the tree will have become slightly over-specified for the job of supporting the remaining canopy.

All of these strategic structural benefits are realised and the physiological health of the tree is preserved because the leaf area is changed by a very small % amount. All that and the structural performance in high wind is refined subtly and measurably enhanced.

The Growth Phase Changes create (in the branch structures that record them), the strategic weaknesses that are retained in the structure of the tree as it grows through maturity.

These things all suggest to me that trees have been designed by evolution to be able to react passively to an extreme climatic event and variable climatic cycles, by simply facilitating dynamic, adaptive and progressive wind pruning as they grow.

The variability of the strength of branch unions originating in the growth phase changes actually enable that to happen.

Let me say that again for impact because this is a really important concept to grasp.

Trees naturally develop strategically weak points in their structure as they grow.

Those points where branches are attached have variable strength specifically so that they can facilitate subtle and progressive branch

failure in high winds because subtle and progressive failure enables the tree to come through a storm rather than failing in total.

Those potential pruning points are naturally distributed around the canopy of the tree and originate in the growth phase changes.

It follows therefore that the branches that were fixed when the tree was young, (during its initial, Apically dominant phase), are the most strongly attached to the main trunk and therefore are the least likely to fail.

Then the first strategic weaknesses were created in the brief period of amorphous growth and branch division that occurs at the first growth phase change. See if you can tell where the various growth phase changes occur in the tree below.

The first is the phase change that is most clearly visible in the structures of many trees and indeed many families of trees. Subsequent growth phase changes are less distinct but are still visible in most trees.

Arborists who can recognise the growth phase changes, can also identify the weaker branch unions to which the most peripheral branches might fail back to in high winds so that by understanding how trees are designed to fail, they can mimic that process.

Then successive growth phase changes break up periods of apically dominant growth and in doing so, create even more branch unions that are of variable strength which appear to me to be there to facilitate wind pruning and give the tree the ability to dynamically adapt and change its size and shape rather than simply fail from the roots.

This negative image shows the structure of the tree well and I have superimposed red lines indicating my estimation of where the distinct growth phases are approximately positioned in the canopy of the tree (in this example, an Oak). Please bear in mind that this is a 2D image of a 3D object and expect it to be easier to track the growth phase changes in a tree when you can move to change your perspective.

Trees facilitate the subtle and progressive reduction of wind loads so that the bulk of the canopy and most of the larger structural elements survive an extreme climatic event and allow the organism to remain alive and able to reproduce long afterwards.

So those relatively weak and even "acute" forks are now rather obviously a benefit because they are all a tree needs to passively survive a strong wind by shedding the most exposed peripheral branches, back to branch forks predominantly (but not exclusively) positioned at the growth phase changes.

Those forks are in fact a survival strategy in action enabling a tree to be modified by wind in a controlled and minimally damaging way. They enable trees to dynamically adapt their structure in response to individual climactic events or changing climactic cycles and co-incidentally this type of pruning simulates the ageing process.

Of course, one aspect of that ageing process is that as branches are lost in storms, the remaining branches are less likely to resonate at the same frequency so dissonant mass damping results.

So, referring to Chapter 3, it becomes clear why 500 million years of evolution have "preserved" such variable and potentially weak structural features and the value, (the anticipation of future benefit), for the tree is that it is likely to survive strong winds rather than fail in total.

In fact, those features are central to a trees structural survival strategy in the fluid and dynamically changeable atmosphere in which they live and in which they have evolved and developed as species over that unimaginable long time.

The weakness contained in the variable strength branch forks becomes the strength by giving the organism the ability to dynamically adapt in a controlled and progressive way to adversities and climactic fluctuations.

Many of these acute or narrow forks have their origins in the Growth Phase Changes. We identify the longest and most exposed foliage bearing branches resulting from those forks and by doing so we suddenly become able to simulate the effects that a strong wind could have on that tree.

So, the emerging revelation contained in all these facts is that "Reduction Via Thinning" is actually "Simulated Wind Pruning".

As such, I believe that it is the only truly sympathetic method of managing the overall size of trees. It's sympathetic because it approximates and copies exactly the same strategy that trees have developed over their immensely long period of evolution.

Reduction Via Thinning is tree pruning the way that evolution has designed trees over hundreds of millions of years to be pruned by wind.

The only difference is that humans are simulating the wind and resulting branches are removed safely and precisely, leaving small wounds that grow over quickly rather than natural rip wounds that can be extensive and are therefore more likely to lead to decay.

Reduction Via Thinning is based on that evolution, understands the way the tree creatively uses adversity and mimics it's likely effects in the way that it modifies the tree in an entirely predictable way. Of course it can also shorten the resonance frequency and can introduce dissonance between the different parts of the tree.

The crucial thing is that by closely mimicking how a tree is designed by evolution to be wind pruned, it produces morphologies which are also very natural in their appearance because it preserves the natural aesthetic characteristics of the particular species.

That simple fact means that tree owners appreciate Reduction Via Thinning if they want to modify the tree and modify risks associated with keeping large trees that they like while also wanting to keep the tree looking as close to how it did before being pruned and while preserving as natural an appearance as is possible. So while achieving all of these strategic modifications Reduction Via Thinning preserves the character and the overall aesthetic appearance of the tree so that afterwards both the tree is recognisable but with the risks associated with the weak branch attachments, modified to favour the owner.

So just like tree evolution, if Reduction Via Thinning had not produced the desired results in my business, (clients, client referrals, repeat clients etc) then that pruning practice would have been lost to my business fossil records.

Reduction Via Thinning was a product that I developed and offered exclusively to my clients. All I can say after 26 years of offering that service is that it got me referrals and did my professional reputation some serious good.

I have employed hundreds of Arborists and trained many of them in these methods. It helped me raise a family and survive over 28 years with my tree care company so I know for certain that if you are an Arborist, it is a very healthy and sympathetic service to offer to your clients and especially once those clients fully understand it.

If I don't take the time to tell them about the insights into trees that support RVT (and the minimum it takes is 10 minutes but usually ends up a long conversation, hence my producing this book!), then the client can only compare the price point.

Happily however, because RVT is actually very efficient (in terms of logistics of the job and therefore man hours) it usually compares very favourably in terms of cost with other pruning methods. After all, logistically the climber is selecting and moving to a few peripheral branches before removing them back to pruning points within the canopy. No "hi-wire" peripheral nibbling that is so difficult and time consuming. This is the same kind of bold strokes that typify what the wind does, literally punching holes in the tree canopy.

So it's predictable, measurable, sympathetic, subtle, efficient and (crucially) it is also usually more cost effective as well.

Oh yes, the last benefit and legacy of Reduction Via Thinning, in comparison to many other pruning methods, is that it does not automatically create the need for follow up tree work, unless you want to, in order to (for example), control a tree's ultimate size and thereby retain it long term at an optimum size for the location (an example Case History of such a size managed tree is included at the end).

It is a progressive and therefore a repeatable specification but once done it does not automatically create the need to do it again that some types of tree pruning do.

In stark contrast pollarding as an extreme example of less sympathetic pruning practice, once done, imposes the requirement to re-pollard periodically throughout the life of a tree or risk branch loss at the pollard point.

Pollarding might be considered the least sympathetic tree management but sadly it isn't.

Pollards can persist for many hundreds of years and although in some regards it creates a grotesque form of winter profile, it can be an acceptable way to have large tree species growing safely along urban or town centre roads. I try to avoid it if possible and that is partially because lopping has been mistaken for pollarding.

This image shows group of freshly lopped trees.

This is not pollarding, in my opinion it's something even worse. Sorry to make you look at this when I am trying to advocate sympathetic pruning but you have to consider the alternative to fully appreciate what I am trying to significantly improve upon.

It is my hope that this book is a step in a positive general direction and that understanding Tree Morphogenesis and Reduction Via Thinning will provide some detailed insights including standardised conceptual models of how trees grow and even a tree road map guiding Arborists to the exact branch and even the exact growth phase change to which a branch needs to be pruned.

It is also my hope that tree work of the kind shown above, is consigned to history as an unenlightened and unnecessarily expensive tree management practice in both the short and long term.

The principles outlined here represent ways to most effectively and reliably communicate ideas between people and especially, between tree owners and tree contractors working to the tree owners specification.

Central to this approach is the tree owner understanding his or her trees then taking control of the specification and by doing so, taking control of the job that he or she has commissioned for their tree.

The most important aspect of that control, is understanding trees and how they are designed by their environment and the need for them to be able to adapt to climactic changes and individual energetic events in spite of the fact that they can't move.

Their ability to passively but dynamically adapt to environmental attrition, comes directly from their structure and specifically from the strategic weaknesses that evolution has rewarded trees that build them into their structure so that they will survive to reproduce in the period immediately after a storm that might have eliminated any species growing according to any other, simpler and more ancient morphological strategy.

The ability to communicate those ideas with clarity between a tree owner and an Arborist and by doing so to define a truly sympathetic action plan where the outcome is certain before the job starts, is the subject of this book. So this conceptual model of how trees grow contains the principles that will allow you to sympathetically manage your trees by more effectively communicating the detail of exactly what you want from your tree care contractor.

Chapter 6

Dose. Enough? Too much? Dose of tree pruning is one thing that is poorly specified, poorly understood and as a direct result, can be interpreted in wildly different ways.

Simulated Wind Pruning sounds plausible as a concept but to what degree should it be done and how do you assess the degree to apply a reliably measured dose of pruning? Well the next issue to cover is quite simply "How much to remove"?

Dose of pruning is something that is so poorly defined that somebody expressing a % in relation to pruning must be aware that as things stand, that % could be interpreted by different Arborist in wildly different ways. In effect specifying a % pruning regime for anything other than Reduction Via Thinning, is effectively meaningless.

I should say here that there are professionals within the industry who will express a simple 20% crown reduction specification in a sympathetic and aesthetically pleasing way, but that is down to their skill and sensitivity rather than any insight imparted from the specifications typically used to supposedly define the job. So the question is, how do you know that you have that sort of sensitive and experienced Arborist? Too many people find out too late that they didn't but the tree retains the signs for many years to come.

The mathematical angle….

Like a geek, or a train spotter, I must have looked slightly strange standing by the side of a road junction with a stopwatch, looking at trees during blustery storms, but gradually and rather self consciously I gathered data that suggested something of greater significance than I could have imagined.

One tree that I measured was a tall Beech that I had been asked by the local council to prune in order to reduce the risks to passing motorists. That tree stood on the crossroads in Whitegate Cheshire where there is a group of very tall landmark trees.

At around 120 feet tall it was imposing but standing in a group of other Beech trees it was not particularly exposed, but it was tall and narrow in form so had a distinct and dominant resonance frequency. That was a tree that I measured that took 4.5 seconds or thereabouts to complete one sway cycle (defining its resonance frequency in seconds).

A few weeks later I performed a Reduction Via Thinning of 15% on that tree.

That percentage of the branches to be removed, (the "dose" of RVT), is assessed by simply estimating the number of foliage bearing branches that are resulting from each successive growth phase change around the canopy. As a tip, I believe that it is more accurate to count the foliage bearing branches just outside of the area that looks like it has the most likely growth phase change branch forks, to prune back to. Then the number of branches to be removed can be defined and limited in that very exacting way.

At each growth phase change the number of branches goes up dramatically but a total number assessed at a similar point along the length of the branches around the canopy will give a total number of branches from which a number of branches to be removed (to achieve the specified % Reduction Via Thinning) can easily be calculated.

To take an example that you should now be familiar with, the Sycamore from Chapter 2.

In the example below, (the tree studied in chapter 2), there are approx 12 structural branches emerging from the straight trunk below the fork that represented the point in time when the apical bud was first lost. Then after that first growth phase change emerge approximately 30 foliage bearing branches. The number of branches emerging from each successive growth phase change rises in a predictable mathematical progression.

Well on that tree, a 15% Reduction Via Thinning would be effected by the removal of just four or five of those branches. The branches targeted to be removed would be the longest and strongest side branches and leaders in that area of the tree and they would be removed in total back to one of the true natural pruning points which are mostly positioned at the growth phase changes.

The projection below shows a proposed RVT of 15% (1) (where the red lines suggest likely points to which the various branches should be removed), with the pruning aimed to be done just outside of the first growth phase change. That means removal of a small number of relatively large branches.

Bear in mind that all of these projections are trying to illustrate a 3 dimensional concept in 2 dimensions. That is why any such guide needs a team including a climber who can follow but also adapt the guidelines creatively and sensitively in the tree.

Compare the projection below to the last one. This projects the same 15% RVT, but this time the pruning is proposed to target pruning points that are around the third growth phase change (classified as RVT15% (3)). The difference is subtle and in effect this is a more sensitive specification that takes a bit more time to complete because the climber is climbing further out in the canopy and making more cuts numerically but removing smaller sections of branch.

From these examples, you should now see that dose cannot be accurately described even by a % RVT, on its own. So by identifying the growth phase change at which the pruning is intended to be concentrated, it is possible to refine a specification and by doing so, refine the resulting tree that is left once the pruning is complete.

Whichever growth phase change is targeted, [RVT 15% (1) or RVT 15% (3)], the removal of that limited number of branches can only change the appearance of the tree very subtly. That limited pruning is going to be good for preserving the natural health and vitality of the tree by preserving leaves all over it. Implicit in that is preserving an attractive appearance of the tree but structurally, does it make a big difference? Absolutely. I believe that it makes a huge difference.

When I returned to that Beech that I measured the resonance frequency of before pruning, a few weeks later when another storm producing the required gusting wind provided the opportunity for me to try to measure the resonance frequency for a second time. When I did that I discovered that something unexpectedly dramatic had happened to the resonance frequency of that tree.

Applying a Reduction Via Thinning of just 15% had shortened the resonance frequency right down to a shade over 3 seconds (from it's previous 4.5 second cycle) although I should say here that my manual timing method was not as accurate as I would like and as mentioned before, I have a limited data set from which I have projected these insights. Even so, the dramatic change seemed to be significant.

The measurements suggested that the pruning resulted in a rise of the resonance frequency of the tree shortening the cycle by over 30% coming as a result of removing just 15% of its peripheral mass.

That apparently disproportionate rise in the resonance frequency was actually typical of other similar measurements that I was able to make subsequently on other trees. That may be significant because it suggests a number of rather important implications.

Trees are self optimising structures which means that they develop the support structure necessary to hold the whole canopy in the air through everything but what are known as "100 year storms," so if a part of their structure is removed, the mechanical elements become mechanically over engineered for the remaining loads.

The different parts of the tree, some having had foliage bearing branches removed some remaining untouched, will have significant variation in their spectrum of resonance frequencies so dissonant mass damping would increase the difference in the reaction of different parts to gusts, which might reduce the amplitude of movement of the whole tree.

Aside from the simple subtle reduction in size which will reduce drag, the loss of peripheral mass would move the centre of gravity down, shortening the time taken for each oscillation cycle just as it does in a metronome.

These very different mechanical benefits all seem to combine cumulatively to produce a disproportionate raising of the resonance frequency in response to what are extremely light and subtle pruning regimes.

My theory also predicted another outcome which was that the benefits, (as expressed by the raising of the resonance frequency of the subject tree), was subject to the law of diminishing returns.

Jargon break

law of diminishing returns (*http://www.thefreedictionary.com/law+of+diminishing+returns*) *n.*

The tendency for a continuing application of effort or skill toward a particular project or goal to decline in effectiveness after a certain level of result has been achieved.

In practice therefore, the lighter the pruning regime, the more significant and profound the effect on the resonance frequency. So once you remove over somewhere in the region of 25%, the resonance frequency has reduced so dramatically that any further pruning produces less and less effect on the resonance frequency of the tree.

So when I first set the upper limit guide for RVT at 25% I did so for other reasons relating to preserving the functionality of the organism, preserving it's vitality by preserving the bulk of it's photosynthesising leaf mass and most importantly, to change the tree and make it subtly smaller while also preserving the character and aesthetic appeal of the tree, but the counter intuitive "less is more" effect on the resonance frequencies of the subject trees instantly made intuitive sense when I discovered it.

After all, in 500 million years such an elegant and efficient solution is exactly what nature and natural selection would be likely to create.

> **Trees grow, adapt to their environment passively reacting to climactic fluctuations by using one of two distinct types of growth phases. In the process they change their morphology at the growth phase changes by dividing branches which slows expansive growth by spreading the resources so the tree grows in all directions rather than just up and out.**

> **They loose peripheral mass most easily by creating variable strength branch forms at the growth phase changes to preserve the central structural mass and main structural branches so they can live beyond the frequency of large storms. That is one efficient and highly evolved BUT SIMPLE organism that is easy to understand once you see how they do what they do and just how efficient they are at it. It is elegant, efficient and based on a simple binary mathematical strategy.**

The hidden result of Reduction Via Thinning, Simulated Wind Pruning or even the natural equivalent is that the tree can become significantly and measurably overspecified for the job of holding the canopy aloft when only a small portion of the canopy is removed.

I am reminded at this point of the pit of the stomach effect of removing just small branches on trees that I have climbed. That's exactly what it felt like, as though I was giving the tree a subtle but tangible mechanical advantage,

I was reducing the amplitude and the resonance frequency of the tree even as I was moving my mass ever upward and so was actively lengthening the resonance frequency as I went, sensing the changes in exactly the same way that I suspect Orangutans do when they are bending and almost breaking branches in order to move through their jungle.

The surprising thing was how little mass of the tree I had to remove to make it feel tangibly different.

I think that this represents a truly adaptable, successful and simple life strategy but if you doubt the significance of Resonance Frequencies, my measurements of them or the implications of this concept, consider this fact.

Trees are self optimising structures. That means that they respond to places in their structure where structural stresses are focussed and reactively thicken the growth increments in that area, laying down more material than it will where stresses are not focussed so as to even out the flow of structural stress throughout their structure.

That accounts for growth adaptations to internal defects, the gradual tapering of the trunk and branches and indeed most of the body language that a tree exhibits.

Body Language of trees is a subject that should interest all tree owners and in my opinion the books of Prof Dr Claus Mattheck or Alex Shigo are very good places to start. The concept describing how a tree equalises forces acting through it is called the Axiom of Uniform Stress. It's not necessary here so no jargon break, instead I urge you to get hold of some of the various books produced by those two gentlemen as they represent books that (like this one does) deliver insights that you can apply to the management of trees.

So if you accept that trees develop the support structure necessary to hold the full canopy aloft through everything but the strongest storms, then, if you remove a small portion of that canopy, two things which are similar but different, result:-

1. The mass and the wind resistance of that small portion of the tree is removed
2. But also, the capacity of the tree to hold up the remainder of the canopy is enhanced by the loss of the mass and wind resistance for which the remaining supporting branch had been adaptively designed.

Those two things are actually distinct and different from each other in ways that I am still trying to fully define. The interesting thing however is that they seem to act cumulatively to dually and distinctly benefit the tree.

So by reducing loading AND increasing the capacity, the tree becomes dramatically over specified structurally for the job of holding up the canopy when just small percentages of the peripheral mass is removed. That simple effect can explain the changes that I experienced with the pit of my stomach and then in the measurements that I was able to make and it may partially explain why small pruning regimes produce such a significant change to the resonance frequency of subject trees.

In fact it's a strategy that we can apply to our own lives.

In my private life and certainly in my business life I like to try to adopt and use that simple ethic because it is so powerful. In fact I would say that it's like compound interest in personal effectiveness.

In practice it works like this, if there is something that I can do better or more easily and more effectively and by taking that on I will reduce or remove a burden that they are struggling with from a colleague, I also increase the capacity in the person who relinquished that burden. If they then take a small burden from me that they can do more easily or better than I can, then we have reduced our respective burdens and increased our respective capacities. We can do more for each other AND individually as a result.

I hope that I can illustrate this by using this book as an example. I am trying to give tree owners information that they need so that they can better understand what their trees might need but more importantly, they will better understand what their trees do not need.

In doing this I am taking on a task (a burden) that is long overdue and it is a task that I am uniquely placed to undertake, that task, re-introducing people to trees and if I'm successful, well I hope that people will hopefully want the service for their trees.

This in turn will encourage contractors to become trained in the art and science of Simulated Wind Pruning as described in Reduction Via Thinning and they will take on my burden to meet the demand for the service from their clients.

In this model, I get to focus on continuing my 28 years of research, tree owners get a service they understand and believe in because it makes perfect common sense to them and Arborists get to do the most personally rewarding form of Arboriculture that there is.

I think that the definition of roles in terms of mutual and sympathetic benefits is a powerful business model that can only gain momentum simply because it benefits everybody that it touches and I adapt that lesson directly from trees.

Trees taught me that. That's incredible to me because I can see the strength in it as a strategy but its true, or rather, its effects and outcomes are true, even if I can't fully explain why yet, although I am working on it.

Small percentage thinning of the canopy therefore have a dramatic effect on the structural capacity of the tree. Even better for the tree it isn't anything that the tree has to actively do, in fact all the tree has to do is expect adversity (500 million years will have done that) and be designed by evolution to turn that adversity into an advantage.

All it has to do is create the opportunity for it to adapt to the fluctuating weather and elegantly adapt to what is inevitable throughout its life, climactic variability in order to survive storms so that it will still be there to set viable seed after the storms when other trees with less highly evolved and adaptable morphological strategies have blown over.

So this is an elegant, simple and highly efficient way that trees adapt through their lives in one place, exploring just how big and wide they can grow to. So how many tree species use this life strategy? Well the diversity and how widely spread the species and families of trees are that use phased growth changes is the subject of the next chapter.

In practice, assessing dose for Reduction Via Thinning is reliable and understandable but it relies on recognising the growth phase changes to add detail relating to the area of the canopy in which the final pruning wounds should be concentrated when the job is complete. With that innovation, dose can be reliably specified and the outcomes projected in the mind of the tree owner and in the mind of the Arborist. That conceptual model guides the outcome and limits unwelcome surprises for the tree owner.

This ability to specify exactly what is removed enables the owner or whoever is specifying the pruning regime to define yet another aspect of dose that is currently impossible without the framework of understanding in this book.

Dose is therefore defined primarily a % of foliage but then it is also possible to define the relative severity of pruning to be applied by specifying the growth phase change that is the target area around one or more growth phase changes, for the Arborist to prune to.

So a light Reduction Via Thinning applied at the first or second growth phase change will involve the removal of just a few relatively large branches.

Contrast that to the same light Reduction Via Thinning but this time applied to the 3rd or 4th growth phase change, (further out along the branches and closer to the edge of the canopy as in the earlier examples). This will involve more climbing and many more pruning cuts.

The effect will be comparable but the second specification will probably cost ever so slightly more and will produce a more subtly modified winter profile whereas the first specification would leave a winter profile that is slightly less subtly modified and therefore will be slightly more recognisable as a pruned tree.

There is one overriding principle and it is the best reason to employ professionally qualified Arborists. I realise as I write that, that the term "professionally qualified Arborist" needs some explanation because it is yet another vague term.

There are NPTC qualified tree climbers who might describe themselves as tree surgeons but NPTC assessments don't cover tree defects or insights into pests and diseases or other tree biology, tree physiology and tree morphology. In other words, NPTC qualifications license people to climb trees safely and perform certain tasks in a tree in a professional way. They are a baseline qualification only.

For me, an Arborist should have qualifications in biological sciences and ideally specifically relating to trees but that's not the end of the story. I have met many Arborists who aren't formally qualified, may be self taught or were just qualified NPTC licensed climbers, who had found their vocation in life and became fascinated by trees.

The key thing is that to be able to undertake a Reduction Via Thinning an Arborist needs to be able to assess the branches proposed for removal given their proximity to the branches and their perspective in the tree so that they can assess defects or identify specific diseases so that they can perhaps modify the specification to remove a defective branch if the branch identified from the ground proves to be in worse condition than another adjacent branch which should be removed instead.

Slavishly following the specification projected from the ground without question will not produce the best results and may leave a latent defect ready to fail, that is why Reduction Via Thinning should only be performed by qualified and / or experienced Arborists.

Qualified Arborists have qualifications that can be assessed.

Experienced Arborists without qualifications are no less valuable and in fact, in many ways, experience is more valuable. However, appropriately committed and talented Arborists without qualifications to validate their service, should ideally have a portfolio of pruning works to illustrate their sensitivity, their bravery, their innovation and diagnostic skills because all can come from practical experience and the development of aesthetic sensitivity.

Qualified or experienced Arborists can adapt Reduction Via Thinning to make it the most sensitive and effective tree management regime bar none. On its own it is a blunt tool that can guide an inexperienced climber but with the requisite professional Arborist applying it, it becomes the sharpest implement in an Arborists or a tree owners conceptual box of tools because it is also adaptable.

Below is a before and image of one of the very first Reduction Via Thinning jobs. This one was done back in 1988.

Yes, it is a heavier % of foliage bearing branches than I advocate now but that was before I realised that the law of diminishing returns applied to tree pruning.

I think we retained the natural flow and the character of this fine Beech tree but sadly I didn't have the foresight to return and snap a picture in the summer following so you will have to take my word for it.

I realize now as I write this, that although I had developed a two page specification for RVT when this job was done, I was limiting the removal of foliage primarily to preserve the health and vitality of the tree while also trying to preserve its aesthetic appeal but essentially (aside from insights gained through my basic Arboricultural training at Reeseheath), I was still pruning by instinct and feel at this stage.

I had yet to realize many of the further insights revealed in this book like the significance of the apical bud, growth phase changes, the benefits that the tree gets from acute and other variable strength of different branch junctions. The whole concept of resonance frequencies in organic structures and the human psychological or perceptual insights that you will soon read about were also absent from my conceptual model of how trees grow.

Chapter 7

Tree genealogy and the family tree of tree families.

There are generally considered to be 52 families of trees. Of those, 2 families are tree ferns which unlike most trees grow from one point only and so are conceptually more like large grasses. I have recently learned of a species of Dandelion or Sunflower (Scalesia pedunculata) that has evolved in isolation on the Galapagos Islands (and in the absence of other tree species whose heavier seeds can't be blown over the ocean to colonise the islands), that has evolved in isolation into a tall tree form with a wooden trunk and branches.

You can learn more about Scalesia here
http://datazone.darwinfoundation.org/media/pdf/22/NG_22_1974_Perry_Sunflower_trees.pdf

Looking at the origin species in each of the families of trees (by which I mean the species that had established themselves as the survivors of the 500 million years of natural evolution rather than the cultivars that have been produced by man since we learned how to cross breed plants), I believe that of the 50 families of classically tree like trees, at least 40 of the families of trees are predominantly composed of species that use the growth phase change adaptive strategy that I have explained, as a fundamental organising principle.

It is also true to say that they all express that fundamental organising principle in subtly different ways and that different species will react to different environmental or other stimuli to prompt the growth phase changes then of course different species will produce characteristically different shapes at and in between growth phase changes. Once growth phase changes are understood, those different expressions can be broken down into components. For example, this approach can help artists to more accurately depict trees and capture aesthetic characteristics that are species specific.

So approximately 80% of the families of trees use this growth strategy but the distribution statistics are even more significant than that because of the remaining 10 families of trees, some of those families are represented by as few as a single tree species. In other words, fossil trees surviving in isolation like evolutionary dead ends.

That means that the few families of trees that do not necessarily display the characteristics that I have described here, appear to be in the process of slow extinction, perhaps (amongst other things), because their life strategy had been superseded by younger families containing species of trees with a more highly evolved form of dynamically adaptive growth that extends their viable life and more specifically, makes decline as protracted as possible. Longevity is implicit in this evolved design and longevity helps the individual tree to reproduce and crucially, to do so after storms when other trees might have been lost which in itself is a devastating advantage for one species to have over another.

All that means that either through convergent evolution (Penguins, Whales and Fish all evolving the same shape because it works best for movement in water) or through divergent evolution (Archaeoptrix the first feathered Dinosaur evolving into the wide range of bird species) the strategy described here represents a fundamental organising principle of most woody plants.

It follows therefore that those 80% of the families of trees that do seem to display the morphological traits that I describe in this book, probably represent well over 90% of the trees that I encounter in the course of my profession and bear in mind when I say that, that there is more diversity of tree species grown to maturity in the UK, than there is anywhere else in the world.

That living tree heritage that we enjoy in the UK came about specifically because of our seagoing history associated with the colonies as well as the efforts of the plant hunters and explorers who scoured the globe for unusual and diverse tree species for plant collections and probably for their own personal glory.

Arboriculture in the UK benefits from a number of factors or convergencies.
- We have the legacy of our colonial past, the wealth that it created used to make grand estates with grand gardens and plant collections.
- Then there are the botanical collections driven by tree scientists which in turn influenced plant breeders to make them widely available which drove plant and tree fashions in such a way that it is possible to approximately date a garden design from the species and specific cultivars included in it.
- Then there is the tortuous planning law and that in turn is an indirect result of 60 million people living on this small island.
- Then there are the geographical aspects most significant of which for trees has to be the Gulf Stream that keeps our winters mild and annual rainfall high.

These factors combine so that Arborists operating in the UK, regularly work on the widest possible range of species in maturity.

Elsewhere in the world only Arborists working on botanical collections will encounter as many diverse species in maturity as UK Arborists encounter on a regular basis.

So we have the organic resources and in recent years there has been a lot of time and money spent on tree research as well. All of this leads me to the conclusion that Arboriculture is going through what will become known as its Renaissance Period.

There are as many expressions of the underlying principles that trees utilise to grow and adapt as there are types of birds that have evolved to occupy different environmental niches, but they are all just subtly different expressions of those fundamental bird like or tree like characteristics.

The differences in the way that individuals express the underlying organising principles characterise the species.

The principles of progressive branch failure facilitated by differentiated structural growth created in growth phase changes in direct response to individual climactic events or even changes affecting the environment over geological timeframes, are fundamental and common to most trees in the wild.

Trees don't live "in the wild" anymore, especially in the UK where there are precious few areas of natural, self regenerating woodland that can trace their origins back thousands of years, so to be complete I must deal with the exceptions even though most are man made.

The exceptions therefore mostly fall into two categories...

1. Species that evolved before the growth phase changes evolved more simple "fractal" like growth patterns.
2. Species produced by man innovating ways to grow and elaborate defects and cross breeding species that would not normally cross breed in the wild.

Exploring the exceptions and the reasons that they represent exceptions, tests the rules and gives perspective to them because to understand why something works it is sometimes very revealing to understand why something else contrasts and doesn't work in quite the same way.

Chapter 8

The exceptions? Yes there are exceptions, but the question is, do they prove or disprove the principles that I describe in this book?

To begin with, there are the variety of species that have been cultivated to have different characteristics by generations of plant breeders. Those plant breeders took the resource of diverse species and cultivated many variants from species that can cross breed in the wild but generally don't, through for example, being isolated to their natural ranges.

Some of the resulting cultivars can even be genetically disadvantaged with growth defects of such magnitude, that it would not reproduce or be able to compete and survive in a primeval forest without human intervention controlling or eliminating competition.

There are many such cultivars in garden centres everywhere. Of course some cross breeding produces offspring with the characteristics of having mismatched genes resulting in cultivars that may be significantly dissimilar to either parent in form and function.

In trees the results of cross breeding can produce what I consider to be genetically defective trees (Lombardy Poplar as an example) but another hybrid the appropriately named "Hybrid Poplar", grows extremely fast and to great size in maturity but can not reproduce easily.

Both of these examples grow very tall, putting them at risk from high winds which results in them being removed from parks and gardens before they have reached full maturity due to the inherent risks that they represent to their owners or people passing close to them.

Plant breeders have a lot to answer for in my opinion. Similarly to the effect that "pedigree" dog breeding has had on our pets, the "exotic", the "hybrid" and the "cultivar" are typically sub-species whose genes have been recombined and bred to refine certain features or suppress certain characteristics.

These "fancy trees" that are in fact genetically damaged in such ways that they would be lost to extinction within a few hundred years if humans were not there to preserve the unnatural conditions that allow the cultivars to survive. I suppose that we could take heart from the fact that in this particular regard (plant cross breeding), humans are responsible for diversifying the number of distinct species.

Let me focus your attention on the Lombardy Poplar. They are almost all a male clone (just to illustrate what a genetic dead end it is) but it makes an interesting tree to explore and study its morphology as a contrast to the natural trees that I am discussing in this book.

Lombardy Poplars came from Lombardy in Italy where they were bred in the aftermath of the Italian Renaissance. The vast wealth and expressions of that Rennaisance wealth led to plant breeding and the development of trees with wildly varying form.

The Lombardy Poplar cultivar is just such a tree with a shape similar to the silhouette of the contextually classical tall and narrow Italian Cypress.

Lombardy Poplar (Populus nigra var italica)

Napoleon then found them useful for lining the historic French N roads because they grew quickly and supposedly disguised the exact number of troops moving around the country by making counting the ranks from a distance more difficult than would be the case if the trees were not there. Napoleon's dedication to warfare and secrecy has left the French countryside and the old "N" roads characterised by these trees. I think that is a shame because that typical Frenchness that is seems to have, has also made this cultivar popular everywhere.

So what's my problem with this particular cultivar? Well these trees grow tall and remain narrow in form. It is as though their ability to differentiate their branch forms from apically dominant upward growth to lateral branching is almost non existent. As a result, they just keep growing up. As plant breeders created this form it is a man made problem.

It is as though the genetic code that gave trees the ability to differentiate its growth through growth phase changes precipitating a distinct change in its morphology, is missing, or has had its growth function impaired so that the tree is incapable of changing its structure in such a way that allows it to spread its branches and by doing so, diversify its branch structure.

Looking up the trunk of a Lombardy Poplar.

Such trees seem to me to hark back to a distant evolutionary past before a tree had evolved the ability to do anything but grow upwards. Growing tall might have been one of the first hurdles to success in the early evolution of trees. That makes it (and other such columnular forms) an interesting subject of a genetic experiment to perhaps identify the growth phase change gene that may be missing from this and other narrow form species.

In practice, owners of these trees must realise that they are naturalised in the relatively arid Italian countryside. When taken from that to a wetter environment, they grow quickly and ever upwards irrespective of the relative exposure of the location.
What makes them an unusual risk is that they are also prone to rotting at the base in the damp UK climate. Those two facts (their continued upward growth and propensity to rot at or close to ground level), make them poor garden trees in the UK in my opinion.

Prostrate forms provide yet another contrast as they grow ever outward out over the ground. Those forms seem not to have the genetic makeup that makes the apical bud grow for the sky. Again seemingly genetically damaged they may shed light on the gene that evolved first to help trees compete to reach the high canopy by the absence of that gene from prostrate forms.

Trees are the largest pets that we will ever own. Crufts and the rigid dog breeding that the "pedigree" title implied has fallen out of fashion (thank goodness) and I think that the same kind of reaction is rightly coming as regards tree species.

Naturally healthy trees, and by naturally healthy I mean both physiologically healthy as well as genetically healthy tree species that can reproduce without intervention, are what we should be proliferating albeit with a few interesting and well chosen specimens chosen for their dramatic potential.

Physiological health is important for the individual in its life struggles but genetic health is important for the survival and evolution of the species. Of the two, in the grand scheme of things genetically healthy trees are ultimately more important although the physiological health of the individual tree is more important for the homeowner because they have to live next to it.

Where these two principles overlap is in the choice of species and planting stock and that is where the consumer has a real role to play.

Yes weird and wonderful cultivars, (essentially "designer" trees cloned or cross bred), are nice to look at and enjoy as contrasts to the less showy but usually healthier and less problematic natural tree species. My advice is to plant healthier natural form trees for the most part and use exotic cultivars, hybrids and clones sparingly and primarily for dramatic effect as highlights to a planting scheme.

So, ultimately those exceptions might just prove the rules that I am revealing here but we will only know for sure when the genetic investigations have been done and the different genes controlling growth phase changes and tree morphology in general, are identified by their absence from prostrate or columnular tree forms.

Don't get me wrong here, Reduction Via Thinning CAN be applied to those columnular forms that grow thin and tall or prostrate forms that can't do anything but grow ever sideways across the ground and it will reliably preserve the shape and character of those forms too.

These are just examples of some of the things that plant breeders have done, the consequences of which only become apparent decades later when the resulting cultivars become mature. They serve to offer a perspective on the nature of the genes that control the morphological traits of trees.

The traits that I describe are most easily observed in native old or ancient woodland, tall woodland rather than scrub but all trees, and even those cultivated artificially and specifically not to have those adaptable growth traits, serve to illustrate the significance of those simple phased growth principles on almost all the trees around us.

The different forms that trees naturally adopt are mostly just different expressions of the phased growth change principle and different tree species create characteristic and recognisable structures at and in between growth phase changes to make the forms that we recognise and identify as certain species.

Then there are the families of Cycads (tree ferns, essentially closer to grasses than trees because they have just one meristem, one point from which growth occurs). Cycads do not follow the growth protocols described in this book.

Jargon break – Meristem http://www.britannica.com/EBchecked/topic/376101/meristem

meristem, region of cells capable of division and growth in plants. Meristem cells are typically small cells the diameters of which in different directions are about equal. They have a dense cytoplasm and relatively few small vacuoles (watery saclike enclosures).
Meristems are classified by their location in the plant as apical (located at root and shoot tips), lateral (in the vascular and cork cambia), and intercalary (at internodes, or stem regions between the places at which leaves attach, and leaf bases, especially of certain monocotyledons— e.g., grasses). Apical meristems are also known as primary meristems because they give rise to the primary plant body. Lateral meristems are secondary meristems because they are responsible for secondary growth, or increase in stem girth and thickness. Meristems form anew from other cells in injured tissues and are responsible for wound healing.

There will inevitably be others and even whole families of tree species that use a variation or an older mode of growth but by far the bulk of trees that you and I will ever see do use these principles and what is essentially an on/off binary system where apical control is generally present guiding growth and periodically absent, resulting in changes in their morphology, differentiating their structure in such a way that it becomes more dynamically adaptable in response to strong winds and statistically more likely to survive an energetic climactic event with the bulk of its structure intact.

There are many environmental niches that trees adapt themselves into but always their form is directly affected by their environment and their reactions in response to fluctuations in their environment so wherever you are in the world, this applies to your trees and influences the shapes that they grow into. For that reason alone it is worth understanding. For that reason I think that it is also worth researching in order for people to come to a much more intimate understanding of the body language of trees.

The intent of this book is to familiarise you with your trees but the next chapter is the one that will show you just how much you already know, how attuned you are already to trees (however little you thought you know about them before reading this book), and it will show you just how you can unlock or simply realise your own built in sensitivity to trees and their morphology.

All of the previous chapters were designed to deliver concepts that I hope are understandable and plausible to you. They are the underlying knowledge necessary to prepare you for what you are about to learn about yourself because as you will find out in Chapter 9, you know more than you could possibly imagine and the instincts that I will re-introduce to you have been evolving in humans and the animals that eventually evolved into humans over many tens of millions of years.

That's me (in the previous picture) standing in the yellow coat at the base of the largest tree I ever felled. Strangely enough, it's an absolutely huge Hybrid Poplar and a beautiful tree without doubt. It's not really a garden tree (for most normal gardens that is), and although not in picture, there were four houses within falling distance.

I had three winches attached to it to make absolutely sure it went where it had to and a policeman in attendance to block the adjacent road.

This below is me (on the left) and my friend Ben Kearsley from Flintshire Woodlands whose guys manned the winches all of whom got blown off their feet by the sudden overwhelming gust of wind that this monster tree created when it fell.

It is hard to describe what it feels like to unleash the kinetic energy stored in a well over 100 ft high 50 tonne plus tree but I can attest that it is surreal in the moment and time becomes extended as things start to move and the tree falls and perhaps as a bi-product of the adrenaline released, your senses become absolutely acute.

As it actually starts to move, you realize that there is nothing you can do, you are a close quarters spectator and you are along for the ride. You rely on all of the detailed planning and setting up of the winches, escape routes, police road blocks and all of the many other details that all have to be absolutely right before you release it from its roots and fell it.

The beers that we enjoyed a short time later at the local pub tasted quite amazing and I seem to remember that Ben was moved to sing for some reason, (but he's like that).

The last picture is a favorite of mine while also being quite sad, but then, as we still do to this day, we would try to make use of the timber that is produced as a bi-product of the sometimes necessary removal of trees.

While I now fell trees reluctantly and only after exploring all other options, I do try to make the very best use of such trees by making the timber available on the www.CraftWoods.co.uk website to craftspeople who make wonderful items of furniture from the wood.

We even make timber framed buildings and all of the innovative things that we do with timber and woodchip are so that we can adapt a very sad old Whaling adage "Nothing is wasted, but the tree".

Sometimes in cases like the one above, I feel like a Whaler (with a conscience) but mostly, when I present a client with the case for keeping a tree which they accept, I feel like Greenpeace.

This dilemma that exists for all Arborists of conscience is something that will be a central theme of the next book in this series but for now I need you to understand that every tree that I have felled left me feeling as though I simply had to put something back to redress the balance so to speak and repay the huge debt that I feel I owe to trees. This book is my first installment towards that debt.

Chapter 9

Looking at AND seeing trees differently.

Starting from scratch, I had to make my own way in so many ways that I take for granted now, but back then (28 years ago) I was just putting one foot in front of the other, trying to earn a living by building a business offering tree care in Cheshire.

I had become trained and had a basic Arboriculture qualification. Over the first two years I got what I can only describe as a feel for trees. As I worked on them, I studied the trees that I thought I had done an aesthetically pleasing job on and did so with great care. I simply wanted to understand what I had done right in ever more detail so that I could come to understand it better and then recreate it for other clients. That process is still ongoing.

The problem was that at that time I was the only professionally trained person on my team and to compound the effect of that, I had a succession of unqualified friends to work with me as my groundsmen.

I had unwittingly fallen into the first trap of growing a business, double booking myself because I needed me on the ground giving aesthetic feedback to guide the job, and in the tree to actually do the job.

So after the initial discussion to plan what we would be attempting, I would ascend the tree and do most of the planned work. The problem came when applying the finishing touches or where other options became apparent while the job progressed.

You see, I was essential in the tree but I also needed to see the overall aesthetic effect before deciding how and where to prune a particular limb or area of the tree.

I could have climbed down periodically to check the shape and identify the next branches to be pruned, but that would have been very hard work. It would have also been very inefficient. Small businesses hate inefficiency and the smaller the business, the more averse to inefficiency it is.

Of course the best way would have been to bounce the aesthetics question off the groundsman but at that early point in my career, he was usually untrained and frankly was usually relatively uninterested in trees or if interested, lacked the technical insights to give the kind of feedback that a climber might find useful.

Frustration drives innovation.

I found that if I shouted down to seek an opinion on the shape and form of the tree only to see the groundsman study the whole tree intensely, I would get a reaction that didn't give me the kind of feedback that I thought I needed. It seemed that too much detailed feedback confused as much as it informed, so I tried something else.

I remember the day I had a breakthrough when I said to the man on the ground "what I need from you is your "*reaction*" to the tree and not your diagnosis of it", adding needlessly "I'm here to do that".

Roles now defined in principle I devised a way to limit what the groundsman had to work with by depriving his senses. So I asked him to turn around so that he faced away from the tree. I then asked him to turn around and glance at the tree for a fraction of a second before turning around again so that he faced away from the tree before telling me what he saw from the image now captured in his minds eye.

The groundsman gave me what he saw perhaps thinking his feedback only loosely useful with vague information like "Well it looks a bit dense/heavy/imbalanced on that side and on the other side there's something that, … er, … just looks wrong somehow!".

Then I would ask him to repeat the exercise at say 90 degrees to the first observation and give me the same brief appraisal and feedback. If possible we would repeat that exercise all around the tree because it only takes a few minutes to do.

The impressions that my groundsmen would convey to me were in fact just what I needed. They were honest reactions to the overall aesthetic image of the tree as it appeared to them and I found the resulting feedback unclouded by trying to see what could be done to address the shape and form of the tree. No diagnosis, just reaction to how the tree looked, which I found to be perfect and just what I wanted.

So a quick glance and a reactive comment meant fast and fluid communication with feedback that was reliably vague but was also strangely, uncannily accurate at identifying issues.

I would take such reactions as a guide as the groundsman and I surveyed the canopy again discussing specific branches, options and how their removal or retention might affect areas of the tree and the overall impression of the tree.

With both of us understanding the tree aesthetically, at least in terms of what appeared to be slightly wrong or imbalanced or varying in density etc etc, we would then try to work out what might improve the aesthetics while I, up in the tree, was able to assess the condition of the branches.

In that separate, interactive diagnostic phase, we would discuss options and likely results of applying those options on the overall shape and character of the tree before deciding on a course of action and then remove the branches/leaders identified.

Invariably from the groundsmans reactions and comments we would identify an area of canopy that was indeed more dense than the rest and we would eventually find a stub or a branch pruned to a side branch that was too small, or had a strange kink off at an angle or something that quite simply jangled with the groundsmans natural sense of form and function just as it had when the groundsmans senses reacted when he just glanced at the tree.

In short, I found that the groundsmans reaction to the image that he had captured in his mind's eye was reliably useful for me. It brought me a purely aesthetic opinion of the general shape, relative density and identified poor form both reliably and quickly.

It was some years later that I finally learned what was actually happening when I asked them to turn and glance before telling me what they saw but it led to what was a discovery that I found to be profoundly uplifting because it showed me just how intimately we are acclimatised to this planets environment and trees in particular and it showed me just how little of our sensory range, we knowingly use in everyday life.

It is all to do with a way that our eyes and our imagination work together to form what is essentially a lost human sense that is dismissed because it has such a subliminal effect.

Sadly it is a sense that over millennia we seem to have learned to override and drown out and that is a real shame because it is a highly valuable and practically useful sense even in this modern world. In fact, it is especially useful in the modern world and well worth understanding and even developing ways of using, in yourself.

The eye has a function or a microscopic movement, called a saccade. Wikipedia says this about saccades…

Saccade

*A **saccade** (pronounced / "sass aide") is a fast <u>movement of an eye</u>, head or other part of an animal's body or device. Saccades are quick, simultaneous movements of both eyes in the same direction.[1]Initiated by eye fields in the frontal and parietal lobes of the brain, saccades serve as a mechanism for <u>fixation</u>, <u>rapid eye movement</u> and the fast phase of optokinetic <u>nystagmus</u>.[1] The word appears to have been coined in the 1880s by French <u>ophthalmologist</u> <u>Émile Javal</u>, who used a mirror on one side of a page to observe eye movement in silent reading, and found that it involves a succession of discontinuous individual movements.[2]*

Function

Humans and many other animals do not look at a scene in fixed steadiness (as opposed to e.g., most birds); instead, the eyes move around, locating interesting parts of the scene and building up a mental, three-dimensional 'map' corresponding to the scene (as opposed to the graphical map of avians, that often relies upon detection of angular movement on the retina). One reason for the saccadic movement of the human eye is that the central part of the <u>retina</u>—known as the <u>fovea</u>—plays a critical role in resolving objects. By moving the eye so that small parts of a scene can be sensed with greater <u>resolution</u>, body resources can be used more efficiently. A human's saccades are very fast.

See also http://www.scholarpedia.org/article/Human_saccadic_eye_movements and http://www.ploscompbiol.org/article/info%3Adoi%2F10.1371%2Fjournal.pcbi.0040031 .

What I believe was happening with my groundsmans reactions was that when they glanced around at the tree, they captured the image of the tree in its entirety in a fast sweep of their eyes, the saccade reflex. Then that image was transferred and held in their minds eye.

Turning away from the tree again they now had only the image that they had caught in their minds eye to process, study and react to.

With nothing but the captured mage their subconscious reaction to that image and their innate sense of form to compare the image against, they were drawn to features that their brain picked out as significant and then they would me what their attention was drawn to in the image. That might be perhaps something that appeared "wrong" to them for whatever reason (the reason was not important, we could study and diagnose that next), but their reaction to their retained image most certainly proved useful as an initial guide.

Crucially, in the absence of a cognitive diagnosis (that they were not necessarily trained to do and in any case I did not want), they could only react instinctively to, and simply say what, their senses saw in the image that they had captured.

In effect it takes much more time to vocalise those impressions than to experience them.

I believe that the origins of this sense is so far back in our evolutionary path that it forms a subconscious and definitely a very primitive reaction to information flooding into the brain from the eyes. It proved so useful that I started thinking about the origins of that saccade reflex.

I imagine that in the forest, jungle or savannah the saccade function was a simple linking of the eyes, the brain and the imagination that could for example, spot a tip of a tail, a paw and a shadow in such a way that our imagination joined up the dots to see a predator lurking and mostly hidden from view.

In that example the reflex reaction would also link into the adrenal glands to prepare the body for action and it is therefore one part of a highly evolved, almost immediate and highly effective, survival instinct using a microsecond sweep of the eyes in conjunction with the minds eye and imagination to prompt decisive action. In this embodiment it is a raw survival skill.

As the processing seems to happen in a primitive part of the brain it will have evolved very early in evolutionary terms, which partially explains why we have mostly forgotten to actively use this sense when of course we are still subject to its influence every day.

Another more benign but universal example that illustrates this point applies to people who dislike spiders. So if you have Arachnophobia this will have special meaning for you because I believe that it is common for people with a Spider phobia, to become agitated before they believe they actually saw the spider.

This could be another example of their eye and their imagination reacting to a glimpse of a shape, or a characteristic movement at the very edge of your vision that their saccades captured and processed in a primitive part of the brain so that their subconscious reacted to alert them to danger. Then adrenaline to facilitate fight or flight response makes the person feel agitated which in itself pre-disposes them to be alert to the danger, agitated and fearful but prepared. Now imagine the same sense applied to a different predator, a big cat in a woodland and I think you will see clearly how it worked well for us for millions of years.

Now instinctively alerted by this sense our ancestors might have looked around and eventually find the thing that their senses told them was there. This can be so subliminal that they might even feel that they sensed the presence of the spider or other threat by some other, supernatural means but it's not, it is just a sense that we have forgotten to make good use of that still has the power to influence us if we allow it.

So in these examples, one extreme and one everyday application you can see one possible explanation of saccades true origin.

Considering another possible expression and function of the saccade reflex, it is possible to realise just how fast acting it is. Consider a football player running down the field of play anticipating a cross from a winger that he hopes to put in the net. He/she has to move to a point in time and space corresponding to where the ball might arrive and in the process the player retains a spatial impression of the ever changing relative position to the other players, the ever changing relation to the net and the trajectory of the ball as it is passed across by the winger.

Given that almost all of the parameters are changing and evolving continually and that all of these parameters affect each other, does it not seem absolutely incredible that human spatial perception can work so fast as to guide the foot to the flying ball in order to propel it into the net? Well that example might illustrate just how fast we can subliminally assimilate and process spatial information (captured by our eyes and processed with incredible spatial accuracy) to guide our actions seemingly without having to think about it. No wonder therefore that this is what I call a forgotten sense, because it is certainly overlooked even though it is clearly something that we all benefit from in some way or other.

It seems to me to be a right brain activity, in other words, an intuitive skill (rather than a sequentially logical thought process which might be associated with left brain activity). Therefore, in a crowd, the left brain might analyse sequentially and logically the facets of the faces of the people that it sees. The right brain would, as the eyes flashed over the crowd, simply see a face that it recognises in total almost instantaneously, as being simply familiar, recognisable and something to which you feel drawn.

This website offers some further insights into right brain vs left brain function - http://www.heraldsun.com.au/news/right-brain-v-left-brain/story-e6frf7jo-1111114603615

In another form of subliminal expression, it is a sense that works underneath our cognitive senses to give us aesthetic feedback on our surroundings all the time and that skill when used in the way that I stumbled upon revealed to me that we all, or at least everybody that I have tested seem to have a very well formed innate sense of aesthetic form and function that we can all tap into if we can just ignore the urge to overuse our brains by actively thinking too much.

I believe that the glance method that I developed and used turns the cognitive brain off by giving it nothing or little to work with and the lack of adequate time effectively suppresses cognitive reasoning and diagnosis in the traditional sense. What is left seems to me to be a raw and primitive but highly informed and instinctively refined gut reaction to the shapes and forms of the tree.

Scientists may not like this because it is difficult to define categorically but it is efficient and highly applicable in the field because it is so practically useful, is easy to do and produces consistent reactions.

I have a feeling that when people look at a Turner or a Constable painting using this sense, they cannot help to react at a subliminal level, to the naturalistic rendition of the landscapes and the trees within it. They either look right or they look wrong. It is a simple as that.

Well in the tree care example, if the image looks wrong for any reason, that subliminal impression primarily guides everything that we then do to make it look less wrong, or even (dare I suggest), make it look "right".

Our appreciation of the natural world seems both universal and consistent and this primitive sense is likely to be one of many underlying that common response to the products of great landscape painters and indeed that common response to trees that we see. The implication is that we all seem to have consistent responses that suggest to me that we all understand trees at this primitive, instinctual level.

That means that when we see something that we might feel is intuitively right or intuitively wrong, we should take serious note of that, study it and understand it. That is because most times, the instincts and opinions resulting from the saccading reflex will guide and influence the next diagnosis phase very effectively indeed.

Using your own saccading instinct by using the glancing method is something that you can do to trick your own brain by suppressing thinking through simple lack of time so that you can learn for yourself what you already know instinctively about trees.

What you need to remember is that none of that knowledge comes out of a book because the ability to recognise both good and bad form are deep inside of your brain literally hard wired into it and intimately connected to various other motor systems like the fight or flight response and your amazing ability to instantaneously process spatial information that pours into your eyes and brain while you move through the world.

In fact I wonder just what we could learn from our subconscious if we refocus our attention on it but here again, it's almost as though we have to stop studying it and stop thinking about the tree to do so.

The glance method has another really valuable role to play beyond the obvious.

Yes, it can reveal insights into the shape and form of the tree from even novice groundsmen that can be reliable and really useful to the climber trying to do an aesthetically pleasing pruning of a mature tree.

However where I believe it makes a profound difference is where it reveals to a groundsman, just how much he already knows about trees and their natural form.

In my experience, this simple trick can make a groundsman feel quite rightly that their own instinctual insights are as truly valuable as they are and that those instincts are already honed by accumulated instinctive knowledge and the way their eyes, brain and imagination combine in a very powerful and useful way.

You see, I believe that everybody is instinctively trained to be a fundamental Arborist and all you have to do to unlock that knowledge within yourself is to give your brain too little time to "study" the tree before you give your instinctive reaction to it.

The beauty of this technique is how it engenders true empathy between the observer and the tree. The feeling of profound closeness and innate understanding turns groundsmen and tree owners into instant intuitive Arborists. We are Arboreal Apes at least in origin and the residual marks of those origins can be glimpsed in such abilities.

Was it Bruce Lee (the famous martial artist and actor) who said "Don't think. Feel!". Well he couldn't have imagined this saccading reflex but I think that it would have resonated strongly with him because it implicitly relies on how the image of the tree captured in your minds eye actually makes you feel.

Now I should say here that in practice, the glance assessment does form part of my instinctive diagnosis but in day to day tree work that is just a brief prelude to a more detailed study and technical diagnosis.

Both are valuable because they use different parts of the brain and both have direct relevance to the job of producing a pleasing, naturalistic tree at the end of the pruning that is being undertaken.

The uplifting message within all this is that the instincts that you possess are unusually good and potentially very valuable to you. So try turning off your brain and becoming more actively and creatively in tune with your instincts, you may learn just how trees affect you at a subliminal level. As you do, you will realise just how honed some of your instinctive skills are.

All of that will illustrate to you just how the evolutionary path that has led to you, has given you some survival and other skills that show where your origins came from and just how we evolved into the profoundly instinctual beings that we are (even if we have stopped recognising and actively finding use for many of our instincts).

Society, business, politics, language and the modern information age have imposed great burdens on our brains but our origins and the skills that improved our success at surviving in what was and to some extent still is a dangerous world, are literally hard wired into it even though we typically override them in daily life.

High time we recognised those skills, rediscovered them and put them to work. We might learn in the process just how much we ignore and (once we stop ignoring it or miss labelling it), we might find out how much we already know. In fact, this is a recurring theme of this book and the various insights.

Topical at the moment in the aftermath of various child abuse scandals, what about helping children to develop and use this skill?

It could be as simple as pointing out to a child how the brain is hard wired to seek out danger, and then tell them that if they are walking down a street and somebody or some thing makes them feel uneasy, they should definitely recognise those feelings as being valid and worth recognising. Then they can try to determine why they feel uneasy (by identifying the danger), so that they can take effective avoiding action.

I won't dwell on that but I have definitely made sure that my children are aware of their own abilities and act on the results of their senses so that they can make themselves less likely to be victims of street crime (for example) by being instinctively wary and responsive to their instinctive brain functions. In my experience, kids are very receptive to reanimating their instincts and I think that is a truly healthy state of being.

I consider myself a sensory creature. Be it the feelings that I had from the resonance frequency of a tree that I experienced while climbing, how that feeling changed if I removed just small side branches, or be it seeing the young tree shape preserved in the mature tree or discovering the glance-assessment method are all based on listening to, studying and understanding my own instinctive responses to things that I experience in my own environment. They are all examples of senses that we humans had mostly forgotten the use of in everyday application and I believe that we learned to overlook them because they defied logical explanation.

Recognition is one thing, then research to discover and illustrate their true value is another but what I hope comes from this is the message that if we don't disregard those "feelings", those instinctive reactions, we may just learn to become sensitive to things that may amaze us.

I'm not a believer in "intuition", at least in the mystical sense of the word. I am however a staunch believer that we possess a broad sensory range that has become mostly redundant in the modern world. I believe that we possess a range of senses that sadly most of us hardly use and when we experience "intuition" we tend to apply mysticism to explain it away and in doing so, dismiss whatever insights are there when in fact we may be experiencing our own sensory range without knowing or recognising it as such.

Reanimation and use of those hidden and forgotten senses starts here with your trees and your interaction with them.

It seems funny to me that in order to reawaken an unused and dormant sense, we have to trick our conscious brains to switch off but that seems to be the case. Once you get used to it I find that I have become far more used to recognising instinctive responses and making effective use of those senses.

Looking at trees using this redundant saccade reflex can really allow you to experience them differently but perhaps it will help you to sense your trees more profoundly as well. You will certainly feel closer to them as a result because you will become aware of a subliminal response that their very shape illicits inside you.

So if Chapter 2 helped you to look at your trees differently, seeing the tree as a culmination of the evolution of generations of that species through time and also as a culmination of that particular trees experience of the events that shaped it in its own life time, then this Chapter is intended to help you to see your trees differently so that you can perceive them in a new/ancient way but most important of all, help you to see just how useful the insights are that you will realise by following these guidelines.

You are a sensory animal and those long forgotten senses can guide you and make you rightly feel more intimately connected to other organisms that you experience in this world.

If you are like me, rediscovering these traits and capabilities within yourself will feel as though you are rediscovering an old friend that you had forgotten existed and that will in turn illustrate to you just what a multi sensory being you really are.

The glance method will quickly fade into something that you do without thinking but the insights that it gives will give true meaning to your use of the way your eyes saccade, capturing an image for your primitive instinctual brain to process for you.

If your eyes return to the tree you just glanced at and you feel drawn to certain areas or features, that is that instinct in action and it definitely has a part to play in efficient, instinctual and truly sympathetic tree management.

It also shows just how intimately we are attuned to the environment and especially the other organisms that inhabit our environment. The connections that we make are tangible but more importantly, they are truly useful in a purely practical way which makes rediscovering yourself in this way such fun to experiment with as well as so practically useful and even commercially advantageous (if you are an Arborist).

Chapter 10

I hope that by now and as a direct result of reading this book, you will now feel that you have a more detailed set of practical insights into trees. Those insights should build and support each other in various ways that all suggest the same thing.

In Chapter Two I showed you a new way to look at tree morphology and recognise patterns of growth that I believe represents a fundamental organising principle underlying the structural adaptiveness of trees to their environment. That morphological trait is represented by the growth phase change between apically dominant "expansive" growth and more lateral growth in the brief moments when apical dominance is removed by climactic and other events in the phased growth changes.

In Chapter Three, I looked closely at acute forks and asked the question "Why do these "defects" still exist if they are really exclusively, detrimental defects?" (which is the prevailing opinion in the Arboriculture industry). That revealed the nature of the failsafe devices that the tree builds into its own structures predominantly at the growth phase changes, to allow parts of the tree to be lost in strong winds rather than the whole tree. The inevitable conclusion is that Acute Forks are not defects to trees. In fact they are an integral part of a tree's evolved, adaptive, structural strategy. They can be latently dangerous to people and property so it is important to recognise them early, but it is equally important to understand their value, to the tree.

In Chapter Four, I discussed resonance frequencies and my findings that suggest that the greatest mechanical advantages are gained for the lightest pruning regimes and that those light pruning regimes change and reduce the risks of failures of large portions of a tree as effectively as heavier pruning regimes do. My observations (from admittedly limited data) also suggest that heavier pruning regimes deliver progressively less and less mechanical benefits (as assessed using the resonance frequency of the tree or part of a tree), cost more because they involve removing more branches and stress the tree more for no short or long term benefit to the tree owner.

The suggestion seems to be where tree pruning % is concerned is that "less is more".

In Chapter Five, I dissected the specification Reduction Via Thinning so that you can see the reasoning underlying it. I hope that you now see that specification as being the closest approximation that exists to "Simulated Wind Pruning" which describes the way that evolution has designed trees to create structures (like variable strength branch forks positioned strategically around the canopy of a mature tree at the first growth phase change and then at subsequent growth phase changes) and differentiate those structures into mostly "structural" in nature or "foliage bearing".

In Chapter Six, the subject of dose was outlined which revealed the simple link between load and capacity of the structurally self optimised tree branch and the fact that where trees are concerned we should trust them more and prune them less.

In Chapter Seven, the number of tree families that display the characteristics that I described was explored to further illustrate the almost universal nature and truly ancient evolutionary origins of this growth strategy but in Chapter Eight, I didn't shy away from the exceptions (that give perspective and could possibly prove the rule by identifying the genes that influence the growth phase changes) which were presented and their structural and genetic limitations explored.

In Chapter Nine, I revealed how we can trick ourselves so as to reach and experience our primitive and instinctive reaction to any natural form. Of all the new insights that I have delivered in this book, I hope that particular one gave you a renewed sense of just how closely your ancestors evolved with trees and within woodland where these senses would have delivered such a valuable survival advantage. Your evolutionary path has left these remnants of the acutely refined survival skills that you can regain and reanimate by effective use. I think this is particularly useful so that you can begin to trust and use your subliminal reactions to tree forms and shapes. Importantly this reaction seems to be common to all humans, at least in my experience but I suppose, with the release of this book, I am about to find out.

These discoveries and their integration in the reasoning behind the tree pruning specification Reduction Via Thinning form the first building block of the Tree Morphogenesis project.

So what are the purely practical outcomes? Well as you will see in the examples that I have included at the end, (the five case histories and more will be made available on the website), Reduction Via Thinning can be used to sympathetically manage the size of a tree. But beyond that, a tree's size and shape can be successively modified over a long period to offset an internal defect (see Case History No. 3) and all while still retaining the character of the tree.

There is one application that is my personal favourite. Imagine a mature tree. A large and majestic tree of great age that had houses built around it. The tree and the owner or their neighbours developed conflicts and frustrations with the tree because since building the houses, the tree had grown larger. Well that tree, if given a light and strategic Reduction Via Thinning, can be subtly modified, subtly reduced, defined and preserved as the character tree that it is. In such a way the benefits that the tree bestows on the neighbourhood and the financial value that a tree can add to a property can be preserved while its deficits are offset. That is truly sympathetic tree (and tree owner/neighbour) care. See Case Histories No. 1 and 2 but also see the video of how we managed a huge Oak for a client in Stockport that you will find on the Tree Morphogenesis website www.treemorphogenesis.com/resources/video-resources.html.

Simulating ageing can improve the aesthetic impact of a tree, adding to its aesthetic impact as Case History No. 4 will illustrate. As an alternative to felling (which is what the client thought he wanted before I presented the alternative), it is always very satisfying to reveal the tree within the older tree and I hope you agree when you see it, that we have revealed a particularly attractive character of that tree within.

Then, for trees that have been unsympathetically managed in the past, Reduction Via Thinning can be used, albeit in heavier than usual percentages, as an excellent alternative to pollarding. In Case History No. 5 because the frequency of repetition necessary to keep the growth parameters within the confines of the space can be predicted, the cost of ownership of the tree involved can be accurately projected so that the owners can budget for the retention of the tree and it's continued confinement within the strategic parameters of the situation within which it exists. All the while, preserving the natural form of the tree both in summer and crucially in winter when the branch structure is visible.

Such trees, managed indefinitely by RVT can be thought of as effectively frozen in time and space. Thus controlled and with the adversities that they can represent modified and the risks that they represent reduced, they can be retained indefinitely so that they are a seed source while also being an environment full of different niches and of course, a wonderful backdrop for our perceptions and a context for our lives. If we can't find room for large trees as they grow, better to help the oldest and largest to continue fit the environment that exists than to simply remove them.

This work it is based almost entirely on my own research, tests and theories that I have developed over more than 28 years of continuous work and interest in trees and the wider natural environment. Up to now, I have used the information in this book to serve my clients and indeed as I said at the start, I used these insights to build a business if not also build a career so 28 years into that career, I know that they work.

The next book in the series is intended to guide how the job is done on a day to day basis. If this book is an introduction to the theory, then the next will cover the practice of Reduction Via Thinning in greater detail.

As such it is oriented for tree contractors and tree owners who want to better understand how their contractors might do the job well. There are as you might expect, many new insights and all practically applicable in the real world, day to day and in a competitive commercial sense, in other words, solutions. I don't sell anything else!

It will improve their knowledge of the job but it will also show just how efficiently RVT can be done and how little it should cost (in comparison to other possible tree pruning regimes) when specified, and then done correctly. Those savings don't only come in the short term because the long term results of poor tree pruning is almost always more tree pruning and management, not less.

Most importantly though, the direct or indirect result of poor tree pruning is ultimately the removal of the tree. The reason? Well I have seen it time and again so that I am absolutely convinced that if we damage or destroy the aesthetic values of a tree, we also kill the owner's will to preserve it. Badly treated trees just quietly disappear and nobody seems to notice because nobody looks at them anymore.

The case histories that I have included here will give some insights to practical applications of Reduction Via Thinning but this introduction is too short and punchy to discuss some of those issues in the depth that the second book will go into.

This book is intended to be an introduction to the theory behind the Tree Morphogenesis Project which is in the broadest sense, a reintroduction to trees.

I feel a need to reintroduce people to trees because I have become aware of a gulf of misunderstanding that has grown between people and trees. That misunderstanding needs to be addressed soon if we are to have any chance of coming to terms with our out of control population boom and our need to get back in synch with the nature of our only biosphere, Earth.

I hope that it has illuminated just how effective, elegant and simple trees and their structural/survival strategies are. Even in the face of climate change and more extreme weather extremes, trees already have their structural contingency plans in place, set there by 500 million years of evolution and there to be recognised and used by tree owners trying to understand and manage (but not necessarily eliminate) tree related risks.

Of course, it is implicit in the structural strategy identified in this book that trees are designed to and will shed branches in gusting or strong winds and consequently, understanding that you should be aware that your first obligation towards trees, is to care for your own safety and either avoid them, or be cautious around them, in the kind of weather conditions that are likely to cause wind pruning. So if you love trees, don't become a statistic that could be used against them.

By understanding those strategies better and reliably simulating them in the tree management as I have applied to my client's trees, I believe that we will be moving to a mode of tree management that is clearly more sympathetic, holistic and sustainable.

In fact I believe that this body of work goes beyond "holistic" in its usual interpretation which is relating to or concerned with the whole organism or with complete systems rather than with the analysis of, treatment of, or dissection into parts (*holistic* medicine attempts to treat both the mind and the body for example) because my meaning of holistic considers the organism as the culmination of its journey through its time on this earth as well as being the culmination of its evolution and the march of is species through time.

Reduction Via Thinning therefore goes beyond holistic because it takes into account the evolution of the organism. It is seeing the tree in time as the culmination of a dynamic reaction process to events as well as the culmination of an evolutionary process with the two concepts separated and conceptually distinct.

Recognising the key aspects and advantages of the almost universal evolved structural strategies of trees and using them in every day tree management is a good few steps beyond any other tree management strategy that exists at present and as a baseline understanding of trees it would set the stage for more insightful and practically applicable exploration of different species and their subtly different expression of the fundamental organising principles described here.

I would be the first to admit that this work has just started. At least I hope that it has but in a really important way, it is actually your reaction to this that will determine if this new area of tree science will grow and find use in the way that people understand trees and how they sympathetically and cost effectively manage them in the real world.

If you feel that you understand your trees better as a result of reading this book, if you can see their development locked into their structures and can see how you might be able to use those features to sympathetically manage your tree, then this book has done what I wanted it to do.

If reading this book is the start of a more intimate relationship between tree owners and their trees, a relationship based on a more detailed and personal understanding of the fundamentals, then I could not ask for more because that is specifically what I have tried to deliver, understanding as I did that it would be the greatest challenge of this work.

If you feel moved to tell me how this book has helped you, or if you have questions, please email me at david@treeadvice.com. If I can help, I will.

If you have done some research that you think compliments or conflicts with some of my findings, I definitely want to hear from you. You see, your insights may improve this work by their inclusion and it is my intention to continually develop this body of work with the help and participation of other innovative researchers. This will happen by the incorporation of any research that moves the science and art of Arboriculture in a positive direction.

For you the tree owner, that will mean that this work will grow and develop but always in ways that you will find enhances your appreciation and experience of trees with emphasis on the practical application of good and truly sensitive tree care. In this context "sensitive" includes all of the range of human senses that can improve our experience, improve our visual acuity and improve our insights into trees.

If you understand what your trees will be least damaged by, what they are designed to survive and most importantly, what they do not need, you will have saved money and your trees will be all the better for applying an informed and minimalist approach to your management of the amenity trees that are in your care.

Further to all of that, you have learned what your tree does not need and that can help you to determine when somebody is offering you a service that is likely to be bad for your tree. So if somebody arrives at your door and asks if you want your trees lopping, you should instantly know what kind of service they offer, as in, a service designed to make them money and usually at your expense in both the short and the long term.

The reason that you know that is because you now know just how significant it might be to remove just a single apical shoot from a tree. You know that such a pruning cut will influence that tree in terms of how it looks and how it grows for the rest of its life and you know that such a cut should be done with a pair of pruning shears rather than a chainsaw.

OK, that's an extreme example and I have nothing against tree loppers, in fact I hope that they read this book so that they too can offer considerate, sympathetic tree works that are efficient, good for the client and naturally compliment the hard work that most tree loppers are certainly capable of.

In the right place, tree loppers (or unqualified tree surgeons) can be highly competitive and very successful, but the right place is hedges or already lopped trees or simple tree removals jobs. Those kinds of work are "Name That Tune" style pricing exercises where the winner says "I can name that tune (remove or lop that tree), in £XXX" where XXX is less than anybody else.

Seriously though, with the information that you now have about the true significance of the first, all controlling apical bud, you know how influential on the shape of the tree in maturity the removal of just the apical bud will be and that knowledge can be used to design a tree into the future. You also know how to identify the structural elements of the tree and the extent of evolved strategies that the tree employs to protect and preserve that structural core specifically so that it can survive individual climactic events and then generate replacement foliage bearing branches

Butterfly wing theory suggests that the flapping of a butterflys wings in the Amazon rain forest can be extrapolated into a storm in the North Atlantic. While no doubt true, at least in principle, the tree equivalent, by which I mean removing just the apical bud from a young tree with a strong single leader, will be an event that will leave clear and unambiguous shapes in the mature tree branch structure throughout the life of the tree. In principle, considering the likely trajectory of buds left at the top of the twig and small twigs below the small pruning cut, it should be possible to predict the shape that the main branches will adopt over the next few decades and do so with a high degree of predictable accuracy. So only lop your young tree if you have stood back and decided for various reasons that you want to and then, do it with hand held pruning devices not chainsaws.

Of course I think that the best way is to let nature and site specific exposure take its course so that the first apical bud is only lost when site specific environmental factors impose themselves on the tree. That way the environment and relative exposure to environmental stresses dictate the size and shape of a tree starting the process described and explained in Chapter 2.

There are many other things that a client can ask a contractor in order to determine the likely quality and value of service that they offer but as the next book will delve deeper into all of the issues revealed here and specifically how to specify and perform Reduction Via Thinning in practice, that book is the most appropriate place to explore them fully.

The outcome might be a range of simple and subtle questions, the answers to which may be extremely useful in order to reveal profound insights to the contractor that is quoting for your tree work contract.

Like any good Lawyer will tell you, before you ask probing questions, you have to already know the answers. Aside from what you have learned in this book, I will propose such Q&A for you to adapt to your situation and many other things that are essential to assess your own trees, specify a tree work regime that will be efficient, effective and sympathetic for you and your trees. Then I will also reveal what I believe to be the best way to engage with a contractor so that there is no doubt about how the job will be done.

It is vitally important to identify a tree care professional and distinguish them from all of the unqualified tree contractors that exist. However please understand, there may be highly sensitive and extensively experienced tree care contractors who cannot display paper qualifications. For them, the revelations in Chapter 9 are there to validate and qualify their experience and their commitment to proper tree care and enable them to compete on a level playing field with conventionally qualified Arborists but it is important to know why you need qualified and or experienced Arborists.

The crucial X factor is the Arborists ability to identify and weigh the significance of defects so that any adapting of the RVT process happens for well considered reasons. After all, if a client taking perspective from the ground suggests one branch to be the one removed, but the Arborist who is closer, in the tree, identifies a branch more likely to be removed by strong winds than the one identified from the ground because of some defect obscured from the ground, then the specification will be modified to more closely approximate simulated wind pruning by that.

Tree pruning can never be a painting by numbers exercise because there are too many interdependent factors in play, all o which have to be weighed. For that reason, I believe that tree work should always be done by trained and experienced climbers, putting their lives at risk using ropes and harnesses to enable them to move in three dimensions within the tree, bound to it by ropes and by need. That close contact and dependency creates empathy that encourages sympathetic, inspired tree care through symbiosis between the climbing Arborist and the tree.

It is the creative interplay between a discerning client and an appropriately qualified or experienced tree care service provider that is crucial to the qualities of the outcome. That creative interplay will be the focus of the next book in this series. Again, like this book, you will not have seen most of the insights anywhere else before, I will challenge a few more long established paradigms and I will deliver more practical understanding that you can apply cost effectively in the real world.

Remember that while I have evolved into a Tree Consultant, I do still climb competitively as a contractor. That means that I'm a pragmatist offering best advice and the most cost effective and reliable solutions all designed to enable me to provide a service that my clients appreciate and a service that would pass the test of time so as to allow me to sell this service throughout my career. Nicest thing of all, where tree services are concerned, principles pay off and form the foundation of a career.

In the next book I will also reveal why I am so completely committed to trees and exactly how my dedication manifests in many ways. Crucially for you the reader, my methods and philosophies can easily be copied and applied to your own enlightened tree care. It all comes down to the revelation that I will reveal in the first few pages and then more fully explain in the last few pages of that book.

The final insight in this book for every tree owner is one that will help decide exactly where would be the best growth phase change to prune a specific branch back to.

It will influence the final shape of a tree, the density distribution of foliage and of course, it will influence and preserve the all important "Character" of the tree if you follow my suggestions.

It is fitting therefore that it should be the last insight in this book assuming as it does that by implication, all of the other insights presented here for the first time, were absorbed.

You now understand how trees are designed by evolution to grow and progressively fail and you know how their resonance suggests that small changes to their size have profound mathematical implications on the tree, so with that conceptual framework clear in your mind, the final insight is simply this;-

Now you have started to hone them, use them but more importantly, place more trust in your instincts and don't dismiss them.

If the branches taper elegantly down to twigs and if the tree still waves around in the wind (only slightly less than it did before), if your eyes feel drawn to it because it just looks right in both summer and winter, then it probably is both aesthetically and physiologically right too and your tree has received the most sensitive and sympathetic care that is available (for now).

David Lloyd-Jones

CHESHIRE TREE SURGEONS / CHESHIRE ARBORICULTURE
www.Arbornauts.com / www.TreeAdvice.com

Tree Care, because we live in a careless world.

RVT Case History 1 - Magnolia

I start with a silly one, a small Magnolia. It had grown to dominate the front garden of my client but had a lovely shape and form typical of the species.

The interesting thing about this one is that it is RVT but done in an unusual way,

It's unusual because unlike large trees there was no limitation on movement and access because it was all done using long pruners and hand held pruning saws from the ground or off short ladders.

The freedom allowed me to do something slightly different, an "outside in" RVT.

Let me explain. Reduction Via Thinning when applied to large trees needs planning, the movements around the canopy,   choreographing for efficiency and speed.

In effect an "inside out" RVT where the tree is climbed from the inside to the points at which it was decided the individual branches would be pruned to. The segment of branch to be removed beyond the growth phase change, is removed and the climber moves on to the next section of the tree.

This Magnolia, like other small trees, was different in that I chose the longest side branches and leaders on each side of the tree, pruned those branches back to the best growth phase change and stood back to assess the changes.

Then as I worked around the tree three or four times the next longest side branch or leader, then the next would be pruned back, gradually reducing it a bit at a time.

In a large tree such pruning is possible but moving a climber around and around a canopy would be difficult, time consuming and therefore expensive.

So this tree affords an opportunity to see what can be done, when gradually reducing a small tree by Reduction Via Thinning in it's purest form, outside in.

It took 2 hours for 2 men including travelling and cost £120 + VAT

The resulting shape preserves the natural looking form, typical of this species, but reduces its overall size in such a way that I think it would be hard to tell the difference and in fact, as this was done when my client was out, they were initially surprised to be told that we had completed the work but then delighted that we had done so only for them to fail to notice. Compliments from clients don't get better than that.

Now I would like to show you something from the other end of the size spectrum, a very large Poplar and this one is a bit more involved than usual because this is a tree that is managed by a group of residents in common space within a farm redevelopment.

I have been formally assessing this tree for about five years for the residents and in fact this is the second Reduction Via Thinning that we have applied to this tree.

So as this is a large tree I assessed the tree from the ground and prepared some perspective images showing where I thought the individual leading branches should be pruned back to. The images were used at the beginning of the job to discuss with the climber and groundsman, the route that the climber would take through the tree so that he visited each segment just once removing what was needed to be removed as he passed through that part of the canopy. Sometimes you have to retrace your steps, but not often.

This is a big tree and it stands within communal space on this gated development so it's the residents who are at risk if it were to fall, so it is to their credit that they thought enough of this landmark tree to ascribe the resources to have it formally assessed periodically and then size managed to reduce the likelihood of major failure.

The test came at my last inspection early in 2011. That revealed that the wound at the base of the tree concealed a large cavity affecting the middle of the tree. OK the thickness of the sound timber around the cavity was such that I had confidence that the tree was strong enough and then we had already nudged the odds by applying a light 10-15% RVT some five years previously, but still, in these circumstances, the odds needed to be nudged further in the residents favour.

I responded by suggesting a further 15% RVT but some residents were not convinced. They actually wanted the tree reducing in height and by a significant amount. At that point in time I was still putting the finishing touches to this book so I could not present it and suggest they absorbed it to see if it changed their perceptions but what I did do was suggest that this tree would form part of the book, if they followed my advice.

That advice had not really changed since my first report and broadly speaking it was that this was a large tree in a windswept location, with a defect at its base. Now as then, it had good leaf density and good leaf colour, so it was and is in good physiological health. So the original light RVT was suggested to alleviate structural stresses and start the process by which we would encourage the tree to develop the lower canopy. Eventually, over three passes in 20 years, the overall height would be reduced while preserving the functionality and vitality of the tree so that the overall size reduction be done while preserving and developing a natural looking lower canopy.

We arrived at a compromise which was a heavy RVT of 25% so I prepared the proposed pruning images that showed red lines to indicate where the final cuts needed to be made.

Of course, I was assuming that no major changes are needed once the climber can see the branches close up.

Then I prepared the modified images showing what the tree would probably look like after the job had been completed and presented these proposal images to the residents for their collective approval.

OK, not the best CGI but such images show a client what they can expect and provide a clear comparison against which to judge the work of the Arborist and groundsman.

Above is an image showing the tree once the RVT of 25% was completed. You will see that the climber made some adjustments to the proposed cuts but overall the effect is as expected. A reduced but still natural looking tree that is unlikely to loose large sections in high winds.

Such predictive images are always going to be subject to changes but it is interesting to
see just how predictable RVT actually is.

On the next 2 pages are the images of the tree once the works were completed so that you
can judge just how close to the proposed shape, we managed to achieve

I think that you should be able to see how the lower canopy is thickening and taking over from the high canopy as the high canopy is subjected to simulated wind pruning. This job took a day for a 3 man team to complete.

This is the tree back in 2006 before we started to apply a light RVT. It had extended side branches and I suspect that a lot of roots had been removed a few years earlier to create the driveway. So the tree was large, had a defect at its base and had lost roots.

Obviously the full natural and flowing canopy is best, but I think RVT comes ca close second to doing nothing at all. Doing nothing was not an option here.

This sequence shows the full natural canopy as it was in 2006 (left) then the tree five years after a light 15% RVT (middle) and then after the further 25% RVT in July 2011 (right).

This sequence shows the full natural canopy as it was in 2006 (left) then the tree five years after a light 15% RVT (middle) and then after the further 25% RVT in July 2011 (right).

RVT Case History 3 - Beech

This 90' tall Beech tree lost a very large secondary leader in the storms that happened in January 2005 and I was asked to look at it to determine if it needed to come out.

The previous image was taken after we had removed the fallen sections but before any climbing repairs were undertaken

It had failed at a major fork in the trunk 2/3 of the way up which left the remaining leader exposed to the prevailing winds from which it had been wind shaded by the now lost leading branch.

On the positive side the damage did not affect the remaining leader and there was no sign of underlying decay in the wound, it was just the wrong, strong gusting wind for this tree.

As a result and even though this tree stands at the intersection of two country roads, I judged that for the time being at least, the tree could be retained as long as it had some of the windload reduced from the exposed remaining leader.

The tree had lost probably 20% of its foliage when it lost the leading branch and we were proposing to remove another estimated 25% in applying the RVT prescribed so there was no doubt that this tree would be stressed.

However, the overall plan was to repeat Reduction Via Thinning in 3 visits over say 20 years and in that time the intent was to effect a significant height reduction over that extended period by removing only small percentages of the foliage in three pruning events over that time.

This meant a race was on to gradually reduce the tree while maintaining its vitality and reducing the size so that by the time the large wound left by the blown out leader developed decay (as it almost certainly would), there would be little branch structure left above the decaying cavity.

So it was reduce it or remove it, so as the client likes this tree, and with the possibility that over 20 years we can modify it's size and shape, and do so sympathetically so that the tree can be retained indefinitely, they decided to prune and not remove.

Complicating the plan is that Beech has limited ability to generate adventitious buds so you have to prune the periphery and by punching big holes in the outer canopy, allow light to penetrate the middle so as to reanimate branches in the process of being suppressed so as to replace lost leaf within the canopy.

The regeneration of leaf within the canopy will facilitate further peripheral pruning while maintaining adequate leaves to produce the products of photosynthesis which is the fuel for cell division, growth and physiological processes like defence.

I prepared pruning diagrams and modified some images to show what the outcome might look like after for the client and then to also guide the climbing team.

This image has red lines indicating to approximately where the climber and groundsman would try to prune the tree.

In this image the sections of branch beyond the prescribed pruning points have been digitally removed to predict the shape of the tree once finished.

The finished result with the specified branches removed. March 2005.

This is how it looked at the beginning of May 2005.

This image was taken in August 2011. I hope that it is obvious what the size and shape of this tree will be after 2 more RVT's of approx 20%. That might take another 16 years but the tree has created the fallback position that we will be revealing.

Another sequence for you to compare the tree in winter 2005 just after the storm took the second leader (left), then the tree a few months later (middle) and then six years later (right). The tree is very actively replacing lost leaf and especially in the lower branches which seem to have gained in leaf density compared to the top of the tree. That is exactly as the specification predicts

RVT Case History 4 – Juniper

To the smaller scale trees, this time a Juniper by a formal pond and blocking the view from the living room out over the garden.

My client's first instinct was to remove this beautiful tree. I persuaded him to give it a second chance by saying that if he didn't like it after I had finished, I would remove whatever was left at no additional charge. It was a safe bet.

Firstly I suggested that the prostrate form conifer to the right be removed because all it did was confused the aesthetics of the Juniper.

Then I proposed a feature pruning of the juniper.

Now, I will admit that this isn't strictly RVT but it is based on the principles so what I was trying to do here is simulate ageing. I was trying to make this tree look older than it really is in order to reduce its density and improve its aesthetic impact.

The image below was taken once the prostrate conifer was removed and the lower branches of the Juniper had also been removed.

These actions both improved visual penetration of the garden and started the process of artificially ageing the tree.

Below you can see me trying to avoid my weight damaging the tree

I was trying not to damage the tree while climbing through it to start to clear out the accumulated leaf litter that such trees gather.

In older, larger trees the wind would do this but as this is small and relatively young, I had to, and while I was doing that I also applied a light RVT of 15% to the canopy.

This work is done by hand and with small hand held pruning saws and it takes time.

However I think that it is worth it if by doing so you can change the appearance of a tree in such a way that you unlock its true aesthetic potential.

I think the finished result works, and in fact I think that without it the garden would have lost a wonderful tree that complimented the whole and being a Juniper, it will be a slow growing and consistent feature of the garden for many decades.

It took just 4 hours to do including the clear up and removal of arisings so you be the judge of whether it was a worthwhile investment ….

In 2006 I was asked by the owner to have a look at his Beech tree and propose some form of sympathetic size management.

One look and the problem is absolutely obvious, it absolutely dominated the front of the house and front garden. Yes, there is a house under there and that house definitely benefits from this very attractive tree!

Usually I would advise simple crown lifting to create space for the house beneath, but this is an old pollard so it is perhaps unwise to suggest encouraging upward growth because of the many potentially weak acute forks between the various leaders. Time for a compromise.

First things first, this tree needed the lower branches removing to alleviate the oppressive imposition of intense shade on the house and residents. I also suggested a RVT of around 20-25% to start the ongoing process of controlling the overall size of the tree.

The tree has outgrown the parameters of the site. It was touching the garage, the neighbours garage and the house.

The telephone wires radiating from the pole (almost lost under the tree) were a minor complication.

This is how it was left in 2006.

Then in 2010 the owner contacted me again. The tree had grown out to about the size it had and he gauged that light levels had reduced to the point where he wanted to do something about it.

The job was the same days work for a 2 man team including clear up. As the pruning regime preserved the aesthetic charm of the tree while controlling its size it seemed that one such pruning lasted 4-5 years.

On that basis the cost of maintenance to retain this tree in what is effectively "suspended animation" by repeated application of a 15-20% RVT, is about £120 a year on average.

I think this tree adds £120 worth of aesthetic appeal to this property (a year), but the important thing for those owners is that they can quantify that expense, secure in the knowledge that their tree apparently responds well to it.

So the second application was in winter. It was dark, bitter and a short day and the photographs reflect that I'm afraid but they reveal the branch structure to illustrate the naturalistic branch structure that remains.

Almost done

Before the second RVT

The next day (wouldn't you know it, sunshine!)

The next images are taken the following June 2011.

The tree has reached or even surpassed its optimum size for the site but by applying Reduction Via Thinning of 15-20% every 5 years it can be preserved and enjoyed by my client, his neighbours and the wider community indefinitely.

I particularly like watching this tree perform in wind because the fully formed side branches and leaders sway around like those of a fully natural tree. Of course, in contrast to a full form natural example, the branches sway but the trunk doesn't. There simply isn't enough canopy left to apply the force needed to get the whole tree to sway.

The other thing that makes RVT so easy is that it is so easy to see exactly which branches will be removed in 5 years time, and the only question being, to which of the natural pruning points within the canopy, the Arborist doing this next time will use.

I will be documenting the progress of this tree over the coming years

I drive past this tree whenever I get chance and it always lifts my day.

A tree and house in uneasy harmony.

The last image that I want to include here is a picture taken in winter 2012 and I want you to see it for one reason.

Bear in mind that this tree has been size managed by applying a heavy 25-30% RVT as alternative to more traditional pollarding, so in effect, it has been heavily pruned.

Beech is sensitive to pruning because it doesn't produce epicormic branches as easily as some species. As a result, they usually react badly to heavy pruning but as you have seen, this tree appears to be a picture of health.

However, there is another test to apply to such trees and you can apply the test yourself as you turn the page by simply glancing at the image before studying what you capture in your minds eye to see if any part of the structures that I have left, jangle with your innate sense of form. That, as far as I am concerned is the ultimate test of any tree that has been size managed twice in six years.

Your test (which is really my test and a test of the information given in this book) is quite simply, does it look "pruned" to you?

Then following that, can you see exactly where each of the remaining primary foliage bearing branches will eventually be removed to?

If you can, then you have absorbed everything that I could have hoped for and you have the ability to apply it to your own trees by specifying something that an Arborist can do in a way that there can be no question about interpretation of how it should be done.

As a direct result, you can now get the tree work that you define as being what you want for your tree and you should be able to spot somebody who might not be qualified to do this with just a few questions. At least, that is my hope.

Epilogue

This era of human development and specifically the last 70 years may well become known in time as the "Chainsaw era". The cheap and very effective chainsaw after all has enabled small humans to fell and use even the largest trees, woodlands and even whole jungles around the world.

No doubt influenced by headlines about the swathes of tropical rainforest removed for agriculture and asset stripping of the timber, there is a growing appreciation of the living cultural heritage that is being lost (see http://membercentral.aaas.org/blogs/qualia/worldwide-decline-large-old-trees-alarms-scientists .

What better time therefore to start to really understand these old trees, manage the risks that they represent and by doing so, manage existing mature trees sympathetically effectively and efficiently and by doing so, make room for both them and us into the future. The continued green and pleasant planet resulting might start with how you understand and manage the trees in your own back yard.

In the next book in this series I will start to examine the other ways to manage trees and compare their effectiveness to that of Reduction Via Thinning.

In the process I will go into a lot more detail on all of the subjects introduced in this book to gradually develop your technical tree knowledge and your instincts by building on from the foundations contained in this book.

Similarly to this book, the next will also be written in plain English with further jargon breaks as necessary and will aim to deliver more practically applicable understanding and solutions that anybody can apply to your trees and their management.

I will also establish a better way to categorise trees relative age that will give a reliably comparable way to define a trees age that everybody will understand. In synch with the work that you have just read it is a way of defining tree ages that would have meaning for trees (if they thought about it).

So, relative age will be explored in the next book in much more detail, using more common sense than ever before and in such a way that the age classifications actually reflect aspects of growth and strategic stages of a trees life. With such a framework of understanding in place we would have age classifications that are subjective and defined by real changes in a tree rather than arbitrary differences, semantics and a range of differing human perspectives.

In short, in the Arboriculture industry, it is about time that we have some standardised terminology to describe trees in every sense and if those classifications bear reference to things that have relevance to trees rather than the current vague and variable age related categories, then they are likely to be universally understood and universally understandable in use.

I will also suggest a way that a tree can be literally mapped in space and time in a brief description. That description would define the tree so that reading it would build a mental image of the tree that will faithfully re-create the tree in the mind of the reader.

An obvious question that comes at me is whether, (as a commercial contractor), do I ever follow other specifications than Reduction Via Thinning, and of course the emphatic answer that may surprise you is Yes, I do.

As a contractor I take on all works, but when I am discussing the options with a client, I do make absolutely sure that I have described and advocated the most sympathetic and the most effective ways to manage the tree in question. I invest my time in doing so.

If that client, complete with the knowledge that what he is paying me to do could be possibly done more sympathetically, if he or she still wants the other way, then I will do it (for a price). You see I am a pragmatic contractor with responsibilities to my employees, but I also have responsibilities to my clients if not also to trees, so I always take the time to explain what I believe to be a more sympathetic and cost effective work proposal so that the client can make informed decisions.

Old joke. "What do tree surgeons and monkeys have in common"?
The answer, …. "They both mess up trees" !

Never a truer word was spoken in jest, you see, tree surgery is at best a compromise and if somebody is paying me to do something, then I feel duty bound to the best that I can for them and sometimes it is best to give the client a reality check to see if they really want to manage their tree at all.

So if Reduction Via Thinning is one end of the spectrum and somebody wants something else but especially if they want something unsympathetic and uninspired, then I make a compelling argument AGAINST TREE PRUNING! You see, I'm no fan of tree surgery even though it is a service on which I have based my career.

Another test of an Arborist is "Best Advice". Professional Arborists are duty bound by a moral code encapsulated by that brief phrase "Best Advice". In short it means that we should offer the tree owner the best advice that we have to give to them. That is even if our best advice is to do nothing.

I have made my career wandering around the North West giving advice that many times resulted in no tree work and that counter intuitive strategy has worked for me long term because when I convince a client that they do not need my help, they tend to recommend me to their friends who do need tree work and they do so with confidence simply because they trust my judgement and my honesty, even when it obviously costs me money.

Best Advice costs nothing long term and in fact I treat each time that I advocate doing nothing, as a long term investment in my company's future. So I have prepared an article for any tree owner to read at the point that they are considering tree work. Its purpose is simply to test their plans before commissioning any tree work because long sightedness is really important when considering a trees future.

This is an example of the kind of practical assistance that I will deliver in the next book and as I already mentioned, it starts with a revelation that may shock many people. Crucially though and just like this book, the focus will be on giving you, the tree owner, the information that you need to take control of the future of your trees.

So if you want to see the article that I have been presenting to my clients to get them to consider their proposed tree work in the broadest sense, to give them strategic perspective that will test their intended actions against the other options that they have, you can, just go to www.TreeMorphogenesis.com where you will find a copy of that and other resources that you can read and or download to your computer.

While you are there I hope that you will decide to subscribe. That way, once the second book is ready for release you will get prior notification which will include some further interesting training which will be sent to my subscribers from time to time to develop their strategic tree knowledge ongoing.

What I will reveal at the beginning of Book 2 is the real reason that I have created this body of work and however you may feel about what I will admit once you have read it, by the end of that book I hope that you will agree that it is the main reason that I have been so dedicated to trees and so successful in my chosen career.

Until then, I hope that reading this work has given you both the feeling as well as the understanding of being more closely aligned with your trees.

There is one final thing in the form of an offer. It is an offer to all Cheshire Tree Surgeons clients. If the contents of this book struck a chord with you and you want a quote for us to handle your tree maintenance or management, then you can reclaim the price that you paid for this book against any invoice for tree work from Cheshire Tree Surgeons.

In other words, this book is free to all Cheshire Tree Surgeons Ltd clients so have a look at the range of services that we offer by visiting www.Arbornauts.com or www.TreeAdvice.com.

From these websites and the innovative products and services that you will find there, I hope that you will find something against which you can redeem the cost of this book because then this book really would be my gift to you and your trees.

As you might expect we try to do everything differently to almost every contractor out there so when we cut a tree we try to make good use of everything so please also visit www.CraftWoods.co.uk and www.Cruck.co.uk where you can find timber converted from the trees that we take down or things made from that timber up to an including timber framed buildings ready to take home and erect in your garden.

If recycling trees interests you, we even run timber framing workshops where you can gain the skills necessary to make traditional timber framed structures for yourself.

If innovative Health and Safety interests you, have a look at www.EnergisedAlert.co.uk as an example of Arboriculture influenced risk management for the electricity industry.

Sadly, on the Kindle platform images are rather small with relatively low resolution and that is a shame because the images really help to illustrate the concepts presented. As a result there will be a hard copy printed version with full size images available from www.TreeMorphogenesis.com as well as some free high resolution versions of the key images.

I sincerely hope that this book has given you insights that enrich your personal experience of trees and give you clear guidance on how to manage your own trees but as mentioned, I do value any criticism or insights that you might have for me after all I did make bold claims at the beginning so have I achieved everything that I set out to deliver to you? My email address is david@treeadvice.com if you want to give me your reaction.

Thank you for reading Reduction Via Thinning. Please revive this book on Amazon as I need your feedback to make the next one even better.

David Lloyd-Jones

References (supplementary references on www.TreeMorphogenesis.com)

The illustrations in Chapter 2 were created by the fine artist and sculptor, Faye Wright.
http://yvonne--faye-wright.artparks.co.uk

Baker C. (1991) Towards a Code of Practice for Determining The Safety of Urban Trees in High Winds. Nottingham University Department of Civil Engineering

Bruel & Kjaer (1988). *Structural Testing Part 1 – Mechanical Mobility Measurements*. Denmark

Council of Tree & Landscape Appraisers 9th edition Guide for Plant Appraisal (2000) International Society of Arboriculture Illinois.

Freyn M. (2006) The Human Touch. Mackays of Chatham plc

Gardener B. (1993). Fundamentals of Airflow Over Trees. Forestry Authority Westonbirt

James. K (February 2008). Trees Wind & Dynamic Loads. *Arborist News*. International Society of Arboriculture Illinois.

Jaynes J. (2000). *The Origin of Consciousness In The Breakdown Of The Bicameral Mind*. Mariner Books.

Kolarik. J. & Coder. K. (April 2008). Wind Load Analysis For Trees. Arborist news. International Society of Arboriculture Illinois.

Lloyd-Jones. D. (1995) *Tree Reduction Via Thinning RVT*. www.TreeMorphogenesis.com

Lonsdale. D. (1999) *Principles of Hazard Tree Assessment*. Department of the environment transport & regions. London.

Mattheck C (1994), *The Body Language of Trees*. HMSO London.

Mattheck C. (1998). *Design In Nature*. Springer-Verlag, Germany

Pink D. (2005). *A Whole New Mind*. Cyan Books

Shigo A (1991), *A New Tree Biology*. Shigo & Trees Associates USA

Shigo A (1986), *A New Tree Biology Dictionary*. Shigo & Trees Associates USA

Shigo. A. (1991). *Modern Arboriculture*. Shigo & Trees Associates USA

Stewart I. (2001). *What Shape Is A Snowflake?. Magic Numbers in Nature*. Weidenfeld & Nicholson

Thomas. P. (2001) *Trees: Their Natural History*. Cambridge University press.

Wardlaw C. (1952) *A Commentary On Turings Diffuysion-Reaction Theory Of Morphogenesis* http://onlinelibrary.wiley.com/doi/10.1111/j.1469-8137.1953.tb05203.x/pdf